American Language Hub

LEVEL 1A
Workbook

with Key + access to Audio

ADRIAN TENNANT

macmillan education

Macmillan Education
4 Crinan Street
London N1 9XW
A division of Macmillan Education Limited

Companies and representatives throughout the world

American Language Hub Level 1A Workbook with Key
ISBN 978-1-380-04695-6
American Language Hub Level 1A Workbook with Key + access to Audio
ISBN 978-1-380-04689-5

Written by Adrian Tennant

The author has asserted their right to be identified as the author of this work in accordance with the Copyright, Designs and Patents Act 1988.

First published 2020

Designed by SPi-Global
Cover design based on an original design by Restless
Cover photograph by Plainpicture/Cultura/dotdotred
Picture research by Emily Taylor

The authors and publishers would like to thank the following for permission to reproduce their photographs:

Alamy/Art Directors p6(9), Alamy/Mode Images p6(6), Alamy/Robert Mora p6(5), Alamy/Tom Viggars p6(7); **BananaStock** p22(5); **Getty Images**/Emad Aljumah p33(3), Getty Images/Carlo Amoruso p4(cr), Getty Images/Thomas Barwick p22(3), Getty Images/Blend Images pp13, 16, 35, Getty Images/Paul Burns p29(3), Getty Images/Peter Cade p24(br), Getty Images/Caiaimage p15, Getty Images/Caiaimage/Martin Barraud p28(2), Getty Images/Nano Calvo p22(7), Getty Images/Cheryl Chan p18, Getty Images/Claudiodivizia p30(tr), Getty Images/George Clerk p28(4), Getty Images/CoffeeAndMilk p11(1), Getty Images/Cultura pp22(6), 25(3), 26, 27, Getty Images/Pablo Blazquez Dominguez p39, Getty Images/Dorling Kindersley p28(5), Getty Images/Richard Drury pp22(2), 25(1), Getty Images/E+ p7(br), Getty Images/Wayne Eastep p29(5), Getty Images/EyeEm p7(tr), Getty Images/FatCamera p22(4), Getty Images/fstop123 p28(8), Getty Images/Gerenme p28(7), Getty Images/Hero Images pp10, 21, 22(8), Getty Images/Hoxton p22(1), Getty Images/Images Bazaar p14, Getty Images/iStockphoto pp17, 23, 34(5,6), Getty Images/JazzIRT p28(9), Getty Images/Jenifoto p29(4), Getty Images/Fabio Lamanna p25(2), Getty Images/Maremagnum p32, Getty Images/Maskot p7(tcr), Getty Images/Mbbirdy p29(2), Getty Images/Nicolas McComber p8, Getty Images/Mint Images p34(2), Getty Images/PhotoDisc p6(8), Getty Images/PhotoAlto/Odilon Dimier p37, Getty Images/Oleh Slobodeniuk p4(br), Getty Images/Chad Springer p20, Getty Images/Stockbyte p11(6), Getty Images/Stone Sub p7(bcr), Getty Images/Paul Strowger p11(2), Getty Images/Punnawit Suwuttananun p33(2), Getty Images/Svetikd p4(tr), Getty Images/The Image Bank p11(3,5), Getty Images/Topic Images p28(3), Getty Images/Guy Vanderelst p30(cr), Getty Images/Klaus Vedfelt p34(1), Getty Images/Venusphoto p28(6), Getty Images/VisitBritain p34(4), Getty Images/VisitBritain/Britain on View p29(6), Getty Images/WendellandCarolyn p6(3), Getty Images/Westend61, p33(1), Getty Images/Simon Winnall p38; **Tara Moore** p11(4); **Scanrail** p6(10); **Shutterstock**/Mega_Pixel p6(12), Shutterstock/MJTH p24(tl), Shutterstock/Pix11 p28(10), Shutterstock/Rawpixel.com p29(1), Shutterstock/Alexander Tolstykh p28(1), Shutterstock/Vladi333 p19; **Stockbyte** p6(2); **Thinkstock** pp6(1,4, 11), 34(3).

Printed and bound in Mexico
by Compañía Editorial Ultra, S.A. de C.V.

2021 2020
04 03 02 01

Contents

VOCABULARY
Countries and nationalities

A Match countries (1–10) with the words in the box.

Brazil Canada China France India
Japan Mexico Spain Turkey US

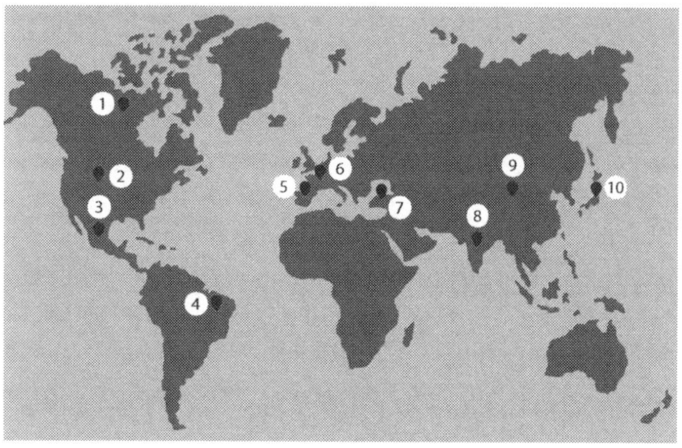

B Choose the correct options to complete the conversations.

a

Megan: Hi, I'm Megan. I'm from Vancouver in [1]*Canada / Canadian*. I'm [2]*Canada / Canadian*.

Keiko: I'm Keiko. I'm [3]*Japan / Japanese*, but I live in [4]*Mexico / Mexican*. This is my husband, Carlos. He's [5]*Mexico / Mexican*.

b

Interviewer: Jin Li? That's an interesting name. Are you [6]*China / Chinese*?

Jin Li: Ha ha! Well, my father is from [7]*China / Chinese*, but my mother is [8]*Britain / British*.

c

Lars: Hello. I'm Lars. I work for ZHEP Technology in Stockholm, [9]*Sweden / Swedish*.

Andreas: Oh, my wife is [10]*Sweden / Swedish*; we go there every year! I'm Andreas, by the way.

PRONUNCIATION
Syllable stress

1.1 Complete the table with the words in the box. Then listen, check and repeat.

Brazil British Canadian Colombia ~~Indian~~
Japan Japanese Mexican Polish Vietnam

Oo	oO	Ooo	ooO	oOoo
		Indian		

GRAMMAR
Simple present *be*: positive and negative

A Complete the sentences with the correct form of *be*.

aren't 'm 'm not is isn't 're

1 Hi! I ________ your new teacher, Mr. Foley.
2 I'm Lucy and this is my sister Mia. We ________ from Sydney, Australia.
3 That's Dev. He ________ from New York.
4 Ha ha! I ________ from Japan, I'm from China.
5 No, my parents ________ French. They're from Belgium.
6 No, she ________. She's Vietnamese.

B Complete introductions (a–c) with the correct form of *be*. Use contractions where possible.

a Hi, I [1]______ Emily and this [2]______ my boyfriend, Noah. I [3]______ Canadian, but Noah [4]______. He [5]______ from the US. In the picture we [6]______ on a skiing vacation in Corvara, Italy.

b This [7]______ a picture of my sister Amy. We [8]______ American, but our parents [9]______. They [10]______ Chinese, but they live in the US. Amy has a boyfriend named Minh. He [11]______ Vietnamese.

c Hi, I [12]______ Elsa and this is a picture of me on vacation. I live in London, but I [13]______ British, I [14]______ from Sweden. I live in an apartment with two friends, Camille and Alicia. They [15]______ both French.

1.2 Arrivals

Where are you?

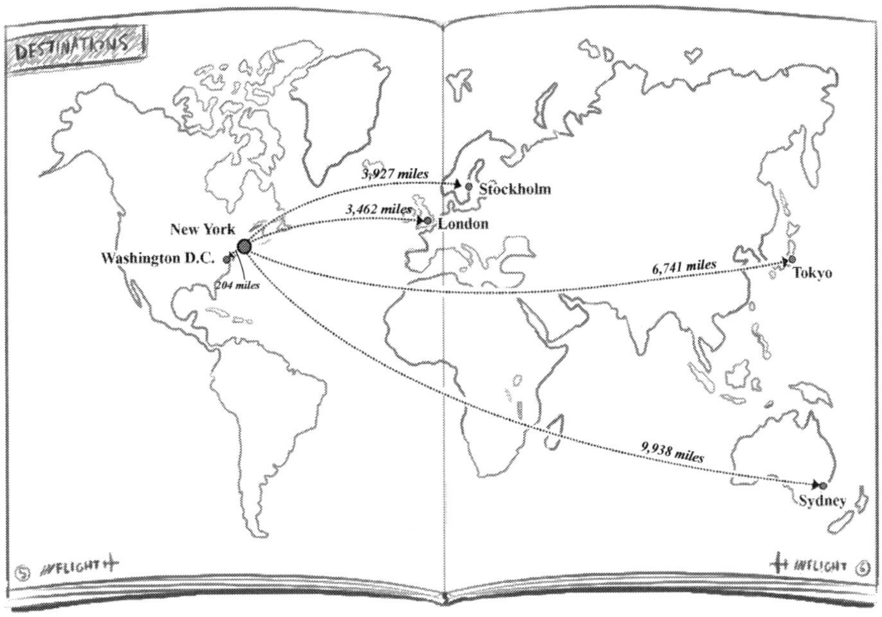

VOCABULARY
Big numbers

A Write the numbers.

1. Nine hundred and thirty-seven. 937
2. Twenty-five thousand, three hundred and twelve. ________
3. Nine thousand, seven hundred and thirty. ________
4. Two and a half million. ________
5. Eighteen thousand, eight hundred and eighty. ________
6. Three hundred and sixteen. ________

B Look at the flight map. Match distances (1–5) with flight paths (a–e).

1 Nine thousand, nine hundred and thirty-eight miles.	a New York to Tokyo.
2 Three thousand, four hundred and sixty-two miles.	b New York to London.
3 Two hundred and four miles.	c New York to Stockholm.
4 Six thousand, seven hundred and forty-one miles.	d New York to Washington D.C.
5 Three thousand, nine hundred and twenty-seven miles.	e New York to Sydney.

PRONUNCIATION
Similar numbers

1.2 **Listen and circle the numbers you hear.**

1. My sister's name is Emily. She's ***13* / *30*** years old.
2. The flight from New York to Tokyo is ***14* / *40*** hours long.
3. It's my father's birthday today. He's ***16* / *60*** years old.
4. It's really sunny outside, but only about ***15* / *50*** degrees.
5. In some countries, ***13* / *30*** is a lucky number.
6. Tickets cost $***18* / *80*** each.

GRAMMAR
Simple present *be*: questions

A Correct the mistakes in each question.

1. Where *are* you ~~are~~ from?
2. Tell me about the city. It is expensive?
3. Is your parents Japanese?
4. Hi, Erin! How you are?
5. It is hot there?
6. What your favorite type of food?
7. Oh, really? Where you are now?
8. You is busy?

B Reorder the words to make questions with *be*.

1
James: *Where are you from?*
(from / where / you / are / ?)
Soo-Jin: I'm from Seoul in South Korea.

2
Sean: ________
(Spanish / you / are / ?)
María: No, I'm not. I'm from Guadalajara in Mexico.

3
Gemma: ________
(Seoul / Paris / far / is / from / how / ?)
Flight attendant: Seoul is 5,568 miles from Paris.

4
Alicia: ________
(you / where / now / are / ?)
Antoine: I'm at the airport.

5
Alex: ________
(favorite / your / food / what's / ?)
Patrick: My favorite food is Indian food. I love it!

1.3 Arrivals
What's in your bag?

VOCABULARY
Everyday items

Label pictures (1–12) with the words in the box.

bottle of water credit card headphones keys laptop magazine cell phone money tissues umbrella wallet watch

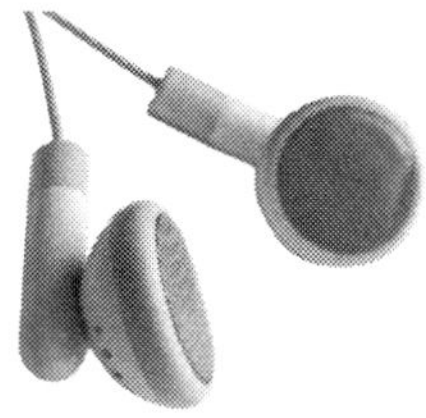

1 ……………………

2 ……………………

3 ……………………

4 ……………………

5 ……………………

6 ……………………

7 ……………………

8 ……………………

9 ……………………

10 ……………………

11 ……………………

12 ……………………

GRAMMAR
a/*an* and plural nouns; *this*, *that*, *these*, *those*

A Complete the sentences with *a*, *an* or – (no article).

1 Heathrow is …………………… airport in London.
2 Take …………………… umbrella – it's raining!
3 Tonya is …………………… French student.
4 There's …………………… money in my backpack.
5 Send me …………………… email when you arrive.
6 Mexico is …………………… country in North America.
7 He travels to a lot of …………………… countries for work.
8 Harvard is …………………… university in the US.

B Complete conversations (a–c) with *this*, *that*, *these* or *those*.

a

João: Hey, is [1]*this / that* your sister over there?
Sam: Yes, it is.
João: Who are [2]*these / those* people with her?
Sam: I think they're her friends from work.

b

Mr. Clarke: Lucas, is [3]*this / those* your bag?
Lucas: Yes, it is. Sorry, sir.
Mr. Clarke: Hmm … and are [4]*that / these* your books?
Lucas: Uh … yes, sir.

c

Airport security: Excuse me! Are [5]*these / those* your watches here?
Passenger: Yes, they are. But [6]*this / that* one there isn't mine.
Airport security: I see … and why do you have six watches?
Passenger: I collect watches. It's my hobby.

PRONUNCIATION
Vowel sounds: /ɪ/ /æ/ /iː/ /oʊ/

1.3 Listen and circle the word in each group that has a different vowel sound.

1	(key)	this	big
2	close	phone	book
3	wallet	bag	that
4	key	it	see
5	watch	that	bag
6	toes	those	tissues

Boarding Pass

Different people, different luggage

SARAH M | 10:17 am

People travel for lots of different reasons. Some travel for fun, others travel for business. But everyone takes something different with them on the plane. Today, I'm at Heathrow Airport to ask people one simple question – What's in your bag and why?

Greg: What's in my bag? Well I'm going skiing in Italy, so I have a sweater for when it's cold. I also have a map, some water and sunglasses. I need to take everything with me, as I don't have lots of money. It's important my bag is easy to carry and isn't heavy. Oh, and I also have some headphones to listen to music on my phone.

Elsa: I travel a lot for work so I have a few very important things in my carry-on bag. I have a laptop, my cell phone and a credit card from work to pay for everything. I also have a magazine because I like to read on the plane when I don't have any work to do.

Ralph: Well, it's difficult as I have to carry things for Harry, here. So I have tissues and other things for a baby. There's not a lot of space for my things, but I do have a cell phone and a newspaper to read when he goes to sleep.

Sandra: What do I have in my bag? I don't really know. The usual things like my phone, money, a bottle of water. I always take a big bag so I can take everything I might need. Let's see … yes, I have an umbrella, some keys and a sandwich. Yes, it's important to have food.

Travel Blog

READING

A READ FOR GIST Read *Boarding Pass: Different people, different luggage* and complete the summaries with Greg, Elsa, Ralph or Sandra.

1 ________________'s carry-on bag has important things for business in it.

2 ________________ has a big bag with money, water and food in it.

3 A lot of things in ________________'s bag are for a baby.

4 ________________ has everything he needs for a vacation in Italy.

Glossary

space (n) an empty or available area

B READ FOR DETAIL Read the article again. Complete the sentences with no more than two words from the article.

1 Greg has a sweater for when it gets ________________ on vacation.

2 He also has some ________________ to listen to music.

3 Elsa uses her ________________ from work to pay for everything.

4 When she doesn't have any ________________ to do on the plane, Elsa reads a magazine.

5 Most of the things in Ralph's bag are for his ________________, Harry.

6 When Harry goes to sleep, Ralph reads ________________.

7 Sandra has a big bag so she can carry ________________ she needs.

8 She thinks it's important to ________________ in her bag.

C REFLECT Answer the questions.

1 What's in your bag today?

2 What do you take with you on vacation?

3 What do you take to work/school?

LISTENING

A LISTEN FOR GIST Listen to a conversation about Vietnam and answer the questions. (1.4)

1 Who does Max talk to?
   a His mom   b His dad   c His sister
2 Where is Max?
   a At a golf club   b On vacation   c At work
3 Why does Max need his coat?
   a Because it's cold
   b Because it's snowing
   c Because it's raining
4 Which topic doesn't Max talk about?
   a The food   b The weather   c The stores

Glossary

grasshopper (n) a large green insect that jumps around on its long back legs
strange (adj) surprising or unusual

B LISTEN FOR DETAIL Listen again. Are the sentences true (T) or false (F)? Correct the false sentences. (1.4)

1 Max is in Hanoi, Vietnam. T / F
2 It's really cold and raining a lot. T / F
3 Max doesn't like Vietnamese food. T / F
4 His mother doesn't want him to eat insects. T / F
5 Max's next destination is Thailand. T / F
6 Max says he needs more money. T / F

C REFLECT Answer the questions.

1 Is Max's mom worried, angry or sad? How do you know?
2 Why does Max say 'Thailand, I think' when his mom asks where his next destination is?
3 Would you like to go to Vietnam? Why/Why not?

FUNCTIONAL LANGUAGE

Greeting people and making introductions

Complete the conversation with the words in the box. Then listen and check. (1.5)

fine how I'm meet this too

Max: Excuse me, is this the train to Sapa?
Emily: Yes, it is.
Max: Oh, great. Thanks. [1] ________ Max by the way.
Emily: Nice to [2] ________ you Max. I'm Emily and [3] ________ is my friend Sophie.
Max: Nice to meet you both. [4] ________ are you?
Emily: Not [5] ________ bad. And you?
Max: I'm [6] ________, thanks.
Emily: So where are you from, Max?

1.6 Arrivals

Fill in a form with personal details

1

Name:	jemma khan
Phone number:	0908766520
Email:	jemmaK@hotmail.com
Username:	jkhan99
Password:	junglekhan1
Confirm password:	***********

2 **ARRIVAL CARD** Immigration Bureau

First name:	Li
Last name:	Wei
Nationality:	chinese
Date of birth:	04/23/1996
Place of birth:	shanghai, china
Occupation:	Student
Passport number:	E15339284

3 **Registration card**

LANTELS HOSPITALITY SERVICES

1 ____________ **name:** Peter

2 ____________ **name:** Evans

3 ____________ **address:** 16 Maple St, Vancouver, BC, Canada

4 ____________ **number:** 778 8614755

5 ____________**:** pete.evans@gmail.com

6 ____________**:** Businessman

7 ____________ **of room:**

Single ☐ Double ☐

8 ____________ **of nights:** Seven

9 ____________ **type:**

Cash ☐ Debit card ☐ Credit card ☐

What is the main reason for visit?

business / tourism / other

10 ____________ **of visit:** One week

WRITING

A Match forms (1–3) with places (a–c).

a at a hotel

b on a plane

c an online account

B Complete form 3 with the words in the box.

Duration Email First Home Number Occupation Payment Phone Last Type

C Look at forms 1 and 2. Find and correct five mistakes with capital letters.

WRITING PRACTICE

Imagine you are at a language school. Complete the registration form. Remember to use capital letters correctly.

Registration form for English classes.

First name: ____________ **Nationality:** ____________

Last name: ____________ **Email:** ____________

Date of birth: ____________ **Phone number:** ____________

Duration of course: 3 weeks ☐ 6 weeks ☐ 12 weeks ☐

Payment type: Cash ☐ Debit card ☐ Credit card ☐

VOCABULARY
Family

Look at the family tree. Complete the sentences with the words in the box.

aunt ~~brother~~ children cousins father grandfather grandmother husband mother parents sister uncle wife

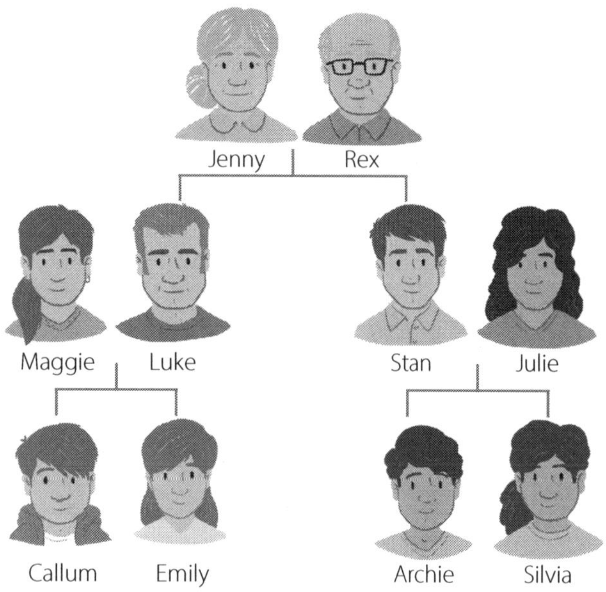

1 Archie is Silvia's *brother*.
2 Maggie is Callum's ______.
3 Luke is Maggie's ______.
4 Jenny is Callum's ______.
5 Stan is Emily's ______.
6 Archie and Silvia are Callum's ______.
7 Rex is Emily and Silvia's ______.
8 Julie and Stan are Archie's ______.
9 Emily is Callum's ______.
10 Jenny is Rex's ______.
11 Maggie is Archie's ______.
12 Emily and Callum are Luke's ______.
13 Rex is Luke's ______.

PRONUNCIATION
/ə/ 'schwa'

2.1 **Listen and underline the /ə/ sound in these words.**

1 cousin
2 famous
3 husband
4 curious
5 actress
6 celebrate
7 family
8 again

GRAMMAR
Possessive adjectives and apostrophes

A Complete the paragraph with the possessive adjectives in the box.

her his its my our their

This is a picture of [1] ______ wife Felicity with [2] ______ friends Bea and Jenna. They come to [3] ______ house every Monday for coffee. [4] ______ children are both four months old. Bea has a son. [5] ______ name is Reuben. Jenna's daughter Evelyn has a toy dinosaur that she takes everywhere. [6] ______ name is Dino!

B Choose the correct options to complete the sentences.

1 My ***parents'*** / ***parent's*** dog is named Rufus.
2 What's your ***sisters'*** / ***sister's*** name?
3 My ***wife's*** / ***wifes'*** favorite food is sushi.
4 My ***grandparent's*** / ***grandparents'*** names are David and Sue.
5 Amazon is a great place to buy ***childrens'*** / ***children's*** books.
6 I think she's married to ***Davids'*** / ***David's*** sister.
7 What color is ***James'*** / ***James's*** bag?
8 I start my new job in two ***week's*** / ***weeks'*** time.

VOCABULARY
Describing appearance

A Match pictures (1–6) with descriptions (a–f).

1 ______

2 ______

3 ______

4 ______

5 ______

6 ______

a Alexa has **long**, **straight** brown hair and glasses.
b James is **bald** and has glasses and a **mustache**.
c Damian has **short** hair and a **beard**.
d Emily's hair is **curly** and **blond**.
e My grandma has short **gray** hair.
f Luke has short **brown** hair and **glasses**.

B Complete the table with the words in bold in Exercise A.

Hair length	Hair type	Hair color	Other

GRAMMAR
have/has

A Complete the sentences with the correct form of *have / has* and *does/does not*. Use contractions where possible.

1 We ______ a small house near Cambridge.
2 ______ your father have a beard?
3 Our hotel room ______ an amazing view.
4 Can you pay? I ______ any money!
5 Do you ______ a big family?
6 Karen ______ curly hair. Her hair is straight.
7 ______ Max have any children?
8 We ______ a lot of friends in the area.

B Reorder the words to make sentences and questions.

1 Ferrari / My / a / uncle / has
______
2 don't / and Tim / children / Amy / any / have
______
3 blue eyes / your / have / mother / Does / ?
______
4 a / He / famous / doesn't / cousin / have
______
5 sisters / my / Both / hair / of / have / blond
______
6 doesn't / sister / today / have / Danielle's / sunglasses / her
______
7 but / doesn't / a car / have / my / , / brother / I
______
8 to / have / store / We / to / time / don't / go / the
______

PRONUNCIATION
have/has

2.2 Listen and circle the correct options to complete the sentences.

1 *He has* / *She has* blond hair and blue eyes.
2 *We have* / *They have* an office in New York.
3 *I have* / *They have* two sisters and one brother.
4 *He has* / *She has* a house in the countryside.
5 No, I think *he has* / *she has* an iPhone 6.
6 I hear *you have* / *they have* a swimming pool.
7 My boss? *She has* / *He has* short brown hair and glasses.
8 Yes, *we have* / *they have* two children – a girl and a boy.

VOCABULARY
Personality adjectives

A Complete the sentences with the words in the box. Use pictures 1–5 to help you.

friendly messy noisy quiet serious

1 My brother is really ________ – his bedroom is terrible!
2 Mike is really ________. He loves to sing and shouts a lot.
3 Silvia is always ________. She never laughs or smiles!
4 Emma is very ________. She talks to everyone and always says hello.
5 Rob doesn't like parties. He's really ________.

B Choose the correct adjectives (a, b or c) to complete the sentences.

1 Penny doesn't like talking to people. I don't know why, but she is ________.
a funny b messy c unfriendly
2 I can't find my keys, because I'm so ________.
a messy b quiet c sad
3 Your sister looks very ________. She's always smiling and laughing.
a happy b serious c neat
4 My brother is really ________. He never stops talking and he's really loud.
a funny b messy c noisy
5 Aroon's ________ because his pet goldfish died.
a friendly b sad c neat
6 Why are you always so ________? You need to smile sometimes.
a funny b noisy c serious
7 Please be ________! I'm trying to finish my homework.
a happy b noisy c quiet

PRONUNCIATION
Syllable stress: adjectives

2.3 Complete the table with the adjectives in the box. Then listen and check.

blond curly different neat quiet serious straight tall unfriendly unhappy

●	●•	●••	•●•

GRAMMAR
Using adjectives

A Reorder the words to make sentences and questions.

1 fairly / person / is / serious / Tristan / a
____
2 are / friendly / roommates / your / very
____
3 is / sister's / messy / my / really / bedroom
____
4 noisy / your / neighbors / very / are / ?
____
5 this / office / very / the / quiet / is / morning
____
6 new / expensive / is / your / apartment / ?
____

B Correct the mistakes in each sentence.

1 My boss isn't a very friend person. He is always shouting!
2 What happened? You're usually neat fairly.
3 Your children are both really talls.
4 My best friend is a very funny. He's always telling jokes.
5 Your parents never smile. They're serious people really.
6 Are you OK? You're quiet fairly today.

Living with the De Lucas

In the US, a lot of people leave the family home when they're 18. However, this isn't true in other parts of the world. In a small village ten miles from Mexico City, three generations of the De Luca family live together. Matt Wallace finds out how they feel about living in the same house.

Mona De Luca is 24 and lives with her younger brother and sister, parents and grandparents in a small four-bedroom house. She loves her family, but finds it difficult to live in a house full of people and wants to move out to share an apartment with her friends.

'1 ______________________________'

Ralph De Luca is Mona's father. He is the opposite of his daughter. He loves living with so many people. 'It's great.

2 ______________________________'

His children say he is serious and he never laughs or smiles. 'It's not true.

3 ______________________________'

Ralph's mother Sophia De Luca is 79, but with her pretty smile and brown eyes, she looks about 60.

'4 ______________________________'

'It's normal for families to live together like this. It can be difficult sometimes, but I'm a happy person and that helps.' Talking about her family, Sophia says,

'5 ______________________________.

They are very noisy.'

READING

A READ FOR GIST Read *Living with the De Lucas*. What is it about?

1 A big family that lives in the same house.
2 A small family that lives in a big house.
3 Different families that live in the same house.

Glossary

generation (n) a group of people, or members of a family, who are about the same age

B READ FOR DETAIL Read the article again. Are the sentences true (T) or false (F)? Correct the false sentences.

1 Mona De Luca lives with two younger brothers. *T / F*
2 She wants to live with her friends, not her family. *T / F*
3 Mona's grandfather is named Ralph. *T / F*
4 Ralph's children think he's a very happy person. *T / F*
5 Mona's grandmother is 60 years old. *T / F*
6 Sophia De Luca says she is a happy person. *T / F*

C READ FOR ORGANIZATION Match blanks (1–5) with sentences (a–e) to complete the article.

a I come home from work, there's always food on the table and the house is really neat.
b I love my grandchildren, but living with them is difficult.
c I love to laugh, but when I get home from work, I am tired.
d I'm too old to live at home, I need my own space.
e When people ask how old I am, they are always surprised.

D REFLECT Answer the questions.

1 Who do you share a house or apartment with?
2 Would you like to live on your own? Why/Why not?
3 What's good about living with your parents and grandparents?

LISTENING

A LISTEN FOR KEY WORDS Listen to a conversation about a wedding. Check (✓) the people Maha talks about.

2.4

- ☐ her sister
- ☐ her brother
- ☐ her grandparents
- ☐ her cousin
- ☐ her parents
- ☐ her uncle
- ☐ her brother's wife
- ☐ her aunt

B LISTEN FOR DETAIL Listen again. Match people (1–5) to descriptions (a–e).

2.4

1 Hamad
2 Fauzia
3 Maha's mother
4 Maha's father
5 Mandy

a has blue eyes and is American.
b has a beard and a mustache.
c looks serious, but is funny.
d has short gray hair and wears glasses.
e is slim and has long black hair.

C REFLECT Answer the questions.

1 How would you describe the different people in your family?
2 Do you like big family weddings? Why/Why not?

FUNCTIONAL LANGUAGE

Making and responding to requests

Complete the conversation with the words in the box. Then listen and check.

2.5

~~can~~ could course dollars not please problem sorry that

Doug: [1] Can I help you?
Maha: Yes, [2] ______. Could I have a coffee with milk and a green tea?
Doug: Of [3] ______. Anything to eat?
Maha: [4] ______ I have a chocolate cookie?
Doug: No, [5] ______. I'm afraid [6] ______. We don't have any left.
Maha: OK, no [7] ______. How much is [8] ______?
Doug: That's 4 [9] ______ and 60 cents.
Maha: Thanks.

WRITING

A Read the email and check (✓) the topics the person asks about.

To: e.parks@netserve.com
Sent: Wednesday February 14, 2018, 10:14 am
From: jjcampbell@freeserve.net
Subject: How's things?

Hi Emma,

How are you? Are you enjoying college? What do you study? I can't remember. Who's in your class? I know you live in an apartment near the university. Who do you live with? What are your roommates like?

Looking forward to hearing from you soon.

Best wishes,

Jenny

- ☐ family
- ☐ friends
- ☐ where they live
- ☐ who they live with
- ☐ what they study
- ☐ who is in their class

B Read Emma's reply. Are the sentences true (T) or false (F)? Correct the false sentences.

To: jjcampbell@freeserve.net
Sent: Saturday February 17, 2018, 6:10 pm
From: e.parks@netserve.com
Subject: re: How's things?

Hi Jenny,

I'm very well, thanks. I'm having a great time at college [1] ________ I'm making lots of new friends.

I'm studying science. It's very difficult, [2] ________ I'm enjoying it. There are 15 of us in the class. I'm friendly with a girl named Sophie. She's great [3] ________ we help each other study. Next year, we have to choose chemistry [4] ________ biology.

No, you're wrong about my apartment; it isn't near the university. It's about 30 minutes away. In the morning we can walk [5] ________ take a bus. The bus takes ten minutes. I have two roommates, Carlos [6] ________ Megan. They are brother and sister, [7] ________ they don't look like each other. Carlos is really nice. He's quiet [8] ________ has short black hair. Megan is very messy [9] ________ noisy.

Write soon.

Love,

Emma

1	Emma is enjoying college.	T / F
2	Emma thinks her classes are difficult.	T / F
3	Next year, Emma will study both chemistry and biology.	T / F
4	Emma lives near the university.	T / F
5	She can take a bus to get to the university.	T / F
6	Sophie is one of her roommates.	T / F
7	Carlos is Emma's brother.	T / F
8	Emma likes Carlos.	T / F

C Complete Emma's email in Exercise B with *and*, *but* and *or*.

WRITING PRACTICE

A PREPARE Imagine you receive an email from a friend asking you how you are. Write notes about:

- what you do
- where you live
- people you live, study or work with

B WRITE Use your notes to write an email to your friend.

VOCABULARY
Everyday activities

A Complete the paragraph with the verbs in the box.

get	get up	go	go	have
have	leave	read	take	watch

My name is Katia and I work as a news reporter. During the week, I [1] ______ really early in the morning because I [2] ______ home at 4:15 am and [3] ______ to work at 5 am. I don't [4] ______ breakfast at home, but I [5] ______ three cups of coffee at work to start my day. I finish work at noon and I usually [6] ______ for a run and then go home. At home I [7] ______ a shower and then [8] ______ a book or [9] ______ TV. In the evening I usually [10] ______ to bed at 8:30 pm.

B Match the beginnings of the sentences (1–5) with the ends of the sentences (a–e).

1 We usually watch
2 Olivia often reads
3 Elaf always listens
4 They usually go
5 I often have

a to the news on the radio every morning.
b coffee with friends from college after class.
c for a walk on the beach on the weekend.
d something on Netflix in the evening.
e the news on her phone.

GRAMMAR
Simple present positive

A Choose the correct options to complete the sentences.

1 I ***live / lives*** in an apartment in the center of the city.
2 My mother ***watch / watches*** TV every day.
3 My wife and I ***listen / listens*** to the same type of music.
4 She ***work / works*** in a clothing store in South Kensington.
5 He ***have / has*** breakfast with his family in the morning.
6 I think they ***go / goes*** to work by train.

B Complete the sentences with the correct form of the verbs in parentheses.

1 My friend ______ (*live*) in Los Angeles with his girlfriend.
2 We ______ (*get up*) early on the weekend and go for a run.
3 I always ______ (*have*) two cups of coffee in the morning.
4 He ______ (*work*) in a small office in the city center.
5 Tom ______ (*like*) to eat fruit for breakfast.
6 My sister ______ (*teach*) English in Hanoi, Vietnam.
7 David and Ahmet often ______ (*go*) swimming on the weekend.
8 Majid is an author. He ______ (*write*) science fiction books.

PRONUNCIATION
Third person -s

3.1 **A** Listen and complete the table with the verbs in bold.

1 Michelle **works** as a writer for a magazine.
2 She **lives** with her husband, Tim, in Washington D.C.
3 He **watches** American football on TV every Saturday.
4 Samantha **has** three cups of coffee in the morning.
5 She **goes** for a run every day after work.
6 My husband **starts** work at 5 am every day.
7 Emily **writes** for a famous fashion magazine.
8 He also **teaches** at the local university.

/s/	/z/	/ɪz/
works		

3.2 **B** Listen and circle the verb in each group that ends with a different sound.

1	(gets)	leaves	goes
2	washes	takes	teaches
3	works	plays	shows
4	looks	starts	watches
5	writes	comes	has

GRAMMAR
Adverbs of frequency

A Reorder the words to make sentences.

1 sleep / a night / I / for / eight hours / usually

______

2 late / class / Ali / for / always / are / and / Milos

______

3 always / Samantha / in the morning / of coffee / three cups / has

______

4 plays / sometimes / soccer / my brother / on the weekend

______

5 really / it / cold / in Thailand / never / is

______

6 video games / in the evening / often / play / I

______

B Use the information in the table to write eight sentences with adverbs of frequency.

	Emily	Ben
listens to music on the way to work	often	always
takes a shower in the morning	never	usually
plays video games on the weekend	rarely	sometimes
goes to yoga classes	always	rarely

1 *Emily often listens to music on the way to work*.
2 ______.
3 ______.
4 ______.
5 ______.
6 ______.
7 ______.
8 ______.

PRONUNCIATION
Word stress

3.3 Complete the table with the words in the box. Then listen and check.

~~breakfast~~ coffee director exercise interesting Japan radio umbrella weekend yoga

●•	•●	●••	•●•
breakfast			

VOCABULARY
Prepositions of time

A Complete the paragraph with *at*, *in* or *on*.

I work as a writer so it is essential I have a routine. I always get up early [1] ______ the morning, but not [2] ______ Sundays. That's my day to relax. In fact, usually [3] ______ the weekend, I don't work, I go to the movie theater with my friends or go to the gym to exercise. Oh, and I never work late [4] ______ night, I'm always too tired. [5] ______ Wednesday afternoons, I sometimes go to the beach – it's beautiful there. Sometimes [6] ______ the afternoon I take a nap; my wife thinks it's funny and says I'm like a little baby!

B Are the sentences correct or incorrect? Correct the mistakes.

1 My boss usually has meetings on the afternoon.
2 I never use my phone in night.
3 Maria usually goes shopping on the weekend.
4 Georgina sometimes goes for a run at Saturdays.
5 I usually take a shower early in the morning.
6 Ravi always finishes work early on Fridays.

GRAMMAR
Simple present negative

A Choose the correct options to complete the paragraph.

This is a picture of me eating dinner with my family last year. Both of my parents were born in China, but they [1]***don't live / doesn't live*** there anymore. They moved to Seattle, Washington, in the US when I was six. I still live in Seattle, but I [2]***don't see / doesn't see*** my parents very often. However, every year, they have a big party to celebrate Chinese New Year so I always go to stay with them for the weekend. Sadly, my brother usually [3]***don't come / doesn't come*** because he lives in Sweden now. The party is always great fun, but my dog Sparks [4]***don't enjoy / doesn't enjoy*** it, because he [5]***doesn't like / don't likes*** fireworks! He does like the food though. My mom loves making traditional dishes, but she [6]***don't make / doesn't make*** dumplings as she knows I [7]***don't eat / doesn't eat*** them.

B Are these sentences correct or incorrect? Correct the mistakes.

1 No, I don't live in the city center.
2 My father don't like science fiction movies.
3 She no listen to music at work.
4 My parents don't have a big house.
5 I not speak Spanish very well.

PRONUNCIATION
Sentence stress

3.4 Listen and underline the stressed words in each sentence.

1 We always have a party on the 4th of July.
2 They don't put up decorations until December.
3 We open our presents in the morning.
4 There's a big parade in November.
5 My mother always makes traditional food.
6 Brad doesn't celebrate his birthday.

VOCABULARY
Big celebrations

Read the sentences and complete the crossword with the missing words.

Down

1 Do people wear … clothes to celebrate New Year's Eve in your country?
2 I always watch the … in Manhattan on the 4th of July.
4 My grandmother wants to have a big … to celebrate her 98th birthday.

Across

3 For Eid al-fitr we eat … food like kofta and shemai.
5 Lots of cities have … to celebrate Saint Patrick's Day. I love all of the dancers and costumes!
6 Do you give … to everyone in your family at Christmas?
7 We always put up … for Christmas. It makes the house look nice.

3.4 Days Reading

Chett Martins

A DAY IN SPACE

By Simon Whittaker August 10, 2018

What's a typical day like in space? We spoke to astronaut Chett Martins to find out.

CM: Do I have a daily routine? The answer is 'yes' – routine is important up here. It doesn't matter where we are, we always get up at the same time. The clocks here show the time back in Houston, Texas. The first thing we do is wash up. We don't have a shower, but it is important to stay clean, so we use liquid soap, water and a towel. After that, we have breakfast, then call mission control to talk about the plans for the rest of the day. We are always busy as there are lots of jobs to do. We usually work for 12 hours a day, so our days are really long.

After we finish work for the morning, we have lunch. In the past, food in space was terrible. Everything came in a tube and tasted disgusting! However, things have changed. Now we eat a lot of the same food we did back on Earth – fruit, vegetables, meat … However, most food is dried so you have to add water. We eat three meals a day and even have snacks like nuts and chocolate. After lunch, we spend a lot of time doing boring jobs like cleaning or making repairs to the equipment. It's also really important to exercise and most astronauts spend two hours a day running or cycling on special machines. I like to exercise in the afternoon after lunch.

That's it really. I love my job and I feel lucky to be one of a small group of people to do such an amazing job. After all, the view is out of this world!

READING

A READ FOR GIST Read *A day in space*. What does Chett Martins write about?

1. The things he does every day.
2. The things he does on special days.
3. The things he wants to do back home.

Glossary

equipment (n) the tools, machines, etc that you need for a particular job or activity
essential (adj) very important or necessary
mission control (n) a group of people who control a space flight from the ground
tube (n) a long container that you squeeze to get thick liquids out

B READ FOR THE MAIN IDEAS Read the article again. Put Chett's daily routine in order.

___ call mission control
___ exercise
_1_ get up
___ have breakfast
___ have lunch
___ repair equipment
___ wash up

C READ FOR DETAIL Read the article again. Are these sentences true (T) or false (F)? Correct the false sentences.

1. Chett has a routine. T / F
2. After getting up he always takes a shower. T / F
3. Chett calls mission control to discuss the plans for the day. T / F
4. The food they eat comes out of tubes. T / F
5. Chett enjoys cleaning the space station. T / F
6. Astronauts usually exercise for an hour a day. T / F
7. Chett thinks he's lucky to be an astronaut. T / F

D REFLECT Answer the questions.

1. What things do you think might be difficult about being in space?
2. Would you like to have Chett's job? Why/Why not?
3. Do you think astronauts do an important job? Why/Why not?

LISTENING

A LISTEN FOR GIST Listen to a conversation about a birthday. Check (✓) the activities Simon suggests. 3.5

- ☐ cook a meal at home
- ☐ go out to eat
- ☐ have a party
- ☐ watch a movie
- ☐ eat special food
- ☐ watch fireworks

B LISTEN FOR DETAIL Listen again. Complete the sentences with no more than three words from the conversation. 3.5

1 Beth's birthday is on ________.
2 Beth is ________ years old.
3 She doesn't think it's a ________ day.
4 She doesn't want a party because she doesn't like ________ of people.
5 Beth doesn't have a lot of ________.
6 Beth suggests they go to see a movie on ________ after work.
7 Simon says the first show is at ________.
8 Simon says he will ________ for 7:15.

C REFLECT Answer the questions.

1 Which of Simon's ideas do you like? Which don't you like? Why?
2 What do you usually do to celebrate your birthday?
3 Why do you think Beth doesn't want to celebrate her birthday?

FUNCTIONAL LANGUAGE

Making and responding to suggestions

A Complete the suggestions (1–4) and responses (a–d) with the words in the box.

about	awesome	great	how	let's	sounds	sure	why

1 ________ don't we go out to eat?
2 ________ about going to see that new Tom Hanks movie?
3 What ________ Friday evening after work?
4 ________ go to the one at 7:15.

a ________! I'll book the tickets for 7:15.
b I'm not ________. I don't have a lot of money.
c That ________ good. Hold on. Let me check what time it's showing.
d Now that's a ________ idea! I love Tom Hanks!

B Match suggestions (1–4) in Exercise A with responses (a–d).

C Listen and check your answers to Exercise B. 3.6

3.6 Days

Write a blog post about your day

A DAY in the LIFE of …

about | archive | contact

Mike Adamson, pilot at XEC Airlines

February 17, 2018 | Leave a comment

I work as a pilot so I don't really have a typical day. I do have a routine, but the times change when I'm in different places around the world.

Wherever I am, the first thing I do after I get up is have a cup of coffee. Before I get dressed I take a shower. After that, I check my flight schedule and have breakfast. I always have fruit and yogurt, as it is important to stay fit and healthy in my job.

I usually work three or four days a week. On the days when I don't work, I get up late. After breakfast, I often go to the swimming pool or gym. Then, I have lunch and take a nap. I like to relax in the afternoon and stay at home or in my hotel room.

When I'm working I take the subway to the airport and try to arrive early. I don't like to be late as my job is very difficult. Finally, after work I always read a book or talk to my wife and children on my computer. I enjoy my job, but I sometimes have to work at night and that isn't easy.

WRITING

A Read the blog post. What does Mike Adamson write about?

1 his work routine

2 his weekend routine

3 his new routine

B Read the blog post again and choose the correct options (a, b or c) to complete the sentences.

1 Mike says he doesn't have a …
 a schedule. b routine. c typical day.

2 He has a cup of coffee after he …
 a checks his schedule. b gets up. c takes a shower.

3 He always eats fruit and yogurt …
 a three or four times a week. b when he's working. c for breakfast.

4 He gets up late …
 a three or four times a week. b when he's working. c when he isn't working.

5 He goes to the swimming pool or gym …
 a three or four times a week. b when he's working. c when he isn't working.

6 When he goes to work at the airport …
 a he gets up early. b he takes the subway. c he takes a nap.

7 He always tries to …
 a stay at home. b talk to his wife and children. c work at night.

Glossary

nap (n) a short sleep, usually during the day

relax (v) to rest

schedule (n) a plan of activities and events and when they will happen

C Read the blog again and underline five sequencing words (e.g. *first*, *after that*, *then*, etc).

D Put Mike Adamson's daily routine in the correct order. Use the sequencing words that you underlined in Exercise C to help you.

___ check schedule
___ get dressed
___ get up
___ go to the gym
___ have a cup of coffee
___ take a shower
___ have breakfast
___ have lunch
___ read a book
___ take a nap

WRITING PRACTICE

A PREPARE You are going to write a blog post about your daily routine. Complete the schedule with six to seven activities you do in a normal day and the times you do them.

Time	What?
	get up and …

B WRITE Use your schedule in Exercise A to write a short blog about your day. Add details and use sequencing words (*first*, *after that*, *then* and *finally*) to explain the order.

4.1 Work and Education

What do you do?

VOCABULARY
Work and jobs

A Label pictures (1–8) with the jobs in the box.

businesswoman dentist engineer hairdresser journalist mechanic nurse teacher

1 ______

2 ______

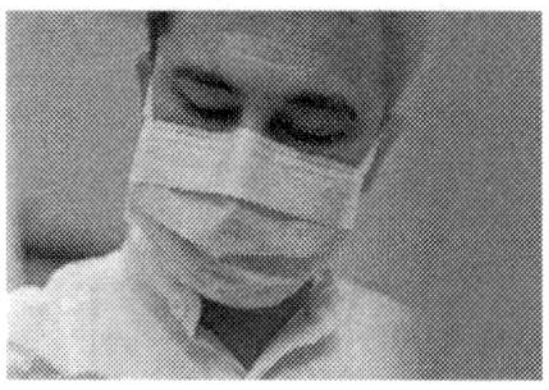

3 ______

4 ______

5 ______

6 ______

7 ______

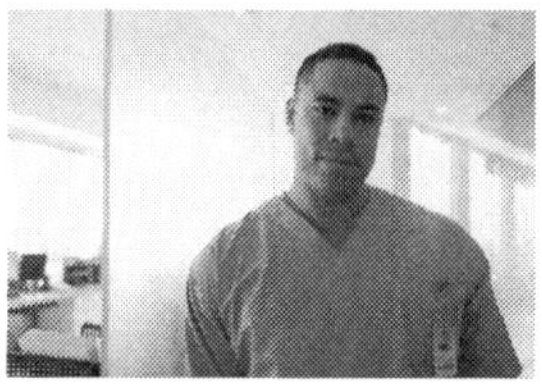

8 ______

B Complete job descriptions (a–d) with the words in the box.

computer home meet meetings office travels wear

a My company has a large [1]______ in central London, but I sometimes work from [2]______ to finish news stories.

b Samia [3]______ a lot for her job and often has [4]______ with people from other companies.

c I [5]______ lots of young people in my job and really enjoy helping them learn.

d Dan works in a hospital and he has to [6]______ a uniform. Sometimes he has to use a [7]______ to check information about his patients.

C Match each job description in Exercise B (a–d) with a job in Exercise A.

GRAMMAR
Simple present *yes/no* questions; short answers

A Match questions (1–6) with short answers (a–f).

1	Do you like your job?	a	No, she doesn't.
2	Do you work at night?	b	No, we don't.
3	Does your father work in the same office as you?	c	Yes, I do.
4	Do your parents know you work there?	d	Yes, he does.
5	Does your mother work from home?	e	No, I don't.
6	Do you and your husband have children?	f	Yes, they do.

B Complete conversations (1–4) with the correct form of *do* or *does*. Use contractions where possible.

1 **Andy:** ______ your brother like his new job?
Ben: No, he ______.

2 **Charlie:** ______ you work 9 am to 5 pm?
David: Yes, I ______.

3 **Emily:** ______ your sister study at a university?
Fran: Yes, she ______.

4 **Greg:** ______ your parents work together?
Harry: No, they ______.

C Reorder the words to make questions with *do* or *does*.

1 in / city / the / Do / center / work / you / ?
Do you work in the city center?

2 full / sister / your / time / Does / work / ?
______

3 work / a / Do / at / uniform / you / wear / ?
______

4 wife / a / work / Does / travel / lot / your / for / ?
______

5 in / company / Does / have / an / your / New York / office / ?
______

PRONUNCIATION
Linking sounds: *do/does*

4.1 **Listen and complete the questions with *Do you*, *Does she* or *Does he*.**

1 *Do you* have to wear a uniform for your job?
2 ______ work at night?
3 ______ travel for your job?
4 ______ use a computer in his job?
5 ______ work in London?
6 ______ work from home?

GRAMMAR
have to / don't have to

A Complete the sentences with the correct form of *have to* and the verb in parentheses.

1 My brother's a firefighter, so he *has to wear* (*wear*) a uniform every day.
2 My brothers are both accountants, so they ________ (*wear*) a suit and tie every day.
3 A self-employed person ________ (*work*) nine to five.
4 Everything in the café is free – our employees ________ (*pay*) for food at work.
5 My sister starts work at 11 am. She ________ (*get up*) early.
6 My boss ________ (*travel*) a lot for her job. She often goes to foreign countries.

B Use the prompts to write questions with *have to*.

1 you / wear / a uniform at work?
Do you have to wear a uniform at work?
2 you / do a lot of / training?
____
3 you / work inside?
____
4 you / pay for tea and coffee?
____
5 you / work nine to five?
____

PRONUNCIATION
Connected speech: *have to*

4.2 **Listen and complete the sentences with the verbs you hear.**

1 Do you have to ________ the phone in your job?
2 Do you have to ________ from nine to five?
3 Does Sarah have to ________ a computer for her job?
4 When do you have to ________ work?
5 Does your boss have to ________ to lots of meetings?
6 What do you have to ________ in your job?

VOCABULARY
Time expressions

A Match the times (1–5) with the time expressions (a–e).

1 5:30 pm
2 12 pm
3 9 am – 5 pm
4 4:55 am
5 12 am

a noon
b early in the morning
c midnight
d late in the afternoon
e nine to five

B Complete the sentences with the time expressions in the box.

early in the morning late in the afternoon midnight nine to five noon

1 John starts work at 6 am every day so he has to get up really ________.
2 What time do you want to meet for lunch? Is ________ too early?
3 I have a really normal office job. I work from ________ with an hour for lunch.
4 OK, well don't stay out too late. Your father wants you home by ________.
5 Every Friday we have a meeting that starts at 2 pm and finishes ________.

GRAMMAR
Question words

A Complete the interview with the question words in the box.

how long how much what when where who why

Dan: [1] ______ do you go to college?
Amy: I study at King's College, Cambridge.
Dan: [2] ______ do you study there?
Amy: I study English literature.
Dan: [3] ______ do you have classes?
Amy: On Mondays, Wednesdays and Thursdays.
Dan: ... and [4] ______ do you want to study English literature?
Amy: I want to be a famous author.
Dan: Oh, really? So, [5] ______ is your favorite writer?
Amy: I like American writers like Donna Tartt and Jonathan Franzen.
Dan: [6] ______ is your course?
Amy: Three years.
Dan: [7] ______ does it cost?
Amy: Nine thousand dollars a year. It's very expensive!

B Write questions using the prompts in parentheses.

1 **A:** Where do you live? (*you / live?*)
B: I live in Kuala Lumpur in Malaysia.

2 **A:** ______ (*you / do?*)
B: I work in a store during the day and I study English in the evening.

3 **A:** ______ (*you / study English?*)
B: Because I want to train as a teacher.

4 **A:** ______ (*take / to become a teacher?*)
B: It usually takes four years.

5 **A:** ______ (*cost?*)
B: I don't know, but it's pretty expensive.

PRONUNCIATION
Word stress: questions

4.3 Listen to the questions and underline the stressed words.

1 Where do you study?
2 What do you study?
3 How long is your course?
4 Who is your teacher?
5 How much do you spend on books?
6 Why do you want to get a degree?

VOCABULARY
Education collocations

A Complete the paragraph with the verbs in the box. There is one verb you do not need.

do get go study take train

Ha ha! This is a picture of me in the library. I'm from Jordan, but I moved to London last year to [1] ______ to college. I [2] ______ medicine at King's College. It's a difficult course, and we have to [3] ______ a lot of exams. That's why I'm always in the library! To [4] ______ a medical certification, you also have to [5] ______ in a hospital for three years – so that's seven years of studying! It's a lot of work, but I think it's worth it. When I'm finished, I can help people anywhere in the world.

B Cross out the incorrect noun in each group.

1 I don't like it when I have to take ~~*a certification*~~ / *an exam* / *a test*.
2 Why do you want to study *a degree* / *math* / *business*?
3 It's difficult to train as *a business* / *an engineer* / *a pilot*.
4 Sarah has to get *a degree* / *an exam* / *a certification* to work as a teacher.
5 Do you want to do *a course* / *a degree* / *a subject* in English?
6 My sister says she doesn't want to go to *college* / *a certification* / *a university*.

4.4 Work and Education

READING

A **READ FOR GIST** Read the job advertisement. Which picture (1–3) matches the ad?

Do you like nature?
Are you happy working outdoors?
We have the perfect job for you.

Marshall Nature Reserve is looking for a special person for the role of park ranger. Marshall Nature Reserve is on a remote island 2,000 miles from the nearest town or city, so it is important you like to spend time on your own.

The salary is $35,000 per year, but remember there are no stores and nothing to spend it on. We provide accommodations and food as well as three round-trip flights a year from the island to Cape Town, South Africa.

Usually a park ranger has to wear a uniform, but for this job it isn't necessary. You always have to get up very early in the morning, not only from Monday to Friday, but on the weekend as well. You have to work long hours but you don't have to worry about traffic jams or arriving late for work.

To apply contact Hans Coetze at h.coetze@marshall.org

Glossary

accommodations (n) a place for someone to stay or live in
nature reserve (n) an area of land where animals and plants are protected
park ranger (n) reserve person whose job is to look after an area of land (e.g. a national park)
salary (n) an amount of money you are paid to do a job

B **READ FOR KEY INFORMATION** Read the ad again. Choose the correct options (a, b or c) to complete the sentences.

1 The nature reserve is …
a on an island. **b** in a town. **c** in a city.

2 There aren't any … on the island.
a people **b** restaurants **c** stores

3 The company does not pay for your …
a accommodations. **b** entertainment. **c** flights.

4 You have to get up early …
a every day. **b** during the week. **c** on the weekend.

5 Park rangers don't have to work …
a outside. **b** long hours. **c** with other people.

C **READ FOR DETAIL** Read the ad again. Complete the sentences with no more than two words from the ad.

1 The ad is for the ____________ of park ranger.
2 The island is ____________ from any towns or cities.
3 Park rangers get paid ____________ a year.
4 The company pays for three ____________ a year.
5 Park rangers don't have to wear ____________.
6 People who want to apply need to ____________ Hans Coetze.

D **REFLECT** Answer the questions.

1 What is your perfect job? Why?
2 Would you apply for the job on the Marshall Island? Why/Why not?
3 What do you think is one advantage and one disadvantage of the job in the advertisement?

4.5 Work and Education

LISTENING

4.4 **A LISTEN FOR GIST** Listen to an interview about work. Check (✓) the topics the speaker talks about.

- ☐ his current job
- ☐ the size of his company
- ☐ his work hours
- ☐ where he lives now
- ☐ where his office is
- ☐ what he eats for lunch
- ☐ the job he would like

4.4 **B LISTEN FOR DETAIL** Listen again. Are these sentences true (T) or false (F)? Correct the false sentences.

1. Graham works as an actor on TV. *T / F*
2. He works from home. *T / F*
3. He has to answer phones in his job. *T / F*
4. He works nine to five. *T / F*
5. He never has time for lunch. *T / F*
6. The company isn't very big. *T / F*
7. He thinks his job is very interesting. *T / F*
8. He wants to be a famous actor in Hollywood. *T / F*

C REFLECT Answer the questions.

1. Why do you think Graham works as a receptionist?
2. Do you think he should move to Hollywood? Why/Why not?

FUNCTIONAL LANGUAGE

Asking for someone and leaving a message

4.5 Put the conversation in the correct order. Then listen and check.

___	**Receptionist:**	Who's speaking, please?
___	**Richard:**	Yes, please. Can you ask her to call Richard from S-REK Ltd at 800-555-0199, please?
___	**Receptionist:**	Hold on a minute, please.
___	**Richard:**	Hello. Could I speak to Hannah Schmidt, please?
___	**Receptionist:**	I'm afraid she isn't available right now. Would you like to leave a message?
___	**Receptionist:**	Good morning. This is Schmidt and Brandt. Can I help you?
___	**Receptionist:**	I'm sorry, can you repeat that?
___	**Richard:**	It's Richard Kershaw.

Glossary

greet (v) to welcome someone with particular words or actions

CAPE ACADEMY

Speaking classes | Exams | Private lessons

Do you want to [1] ______ a language or improve your language [2] ______?

We provide courses in [3] ______ languages – English, French, Spanish and Italian.

Choose a time that works for you. At Cape Academy, we offer classes in the [4] ______, afternoon and the evening.

For more information, [5] ______ Gabriella Souza at g.souza@language.net.sa

WRITING

A Complete the advertisement with the words in the box.

contact four learn morning skills

B You are going to read a reply to the ad in Exercise A. Check (✓) the topics you think the writer will ask about. Then read and check.

- [ ] time of classes
- [ ] what books they use
- [ ] how much the classes cost
- [ ] computer skills
- [ ] the name of the teacher
- [ ] what languages they teach

To: g.souza@language.net.sa
Sent: February 17, 2018, 12:40 pm
From: p.hines@freenett.co.sa
Subject: Language classes

Dear Ms. Souza,

I am writing to ask about your language classes First what languages do you offer Do you have French classes Second, when are your classes I am free in the evenings and on the weekend Do you have classes on Saturdays or Sundays? Finally, how much does the course cost?

I look forward to hearing from you.
All the best,
Pieter Hines

C Read the email again. Correct six mistakes by adding question marks, commas and periods.

D Number the stages of the email in Exercise B.

- ___ Asking about the cost of the courses
- ___ Asking about the language courses on offer
- ___ Greeting and the name of the person you are writing to
- ___ Reason for writing
- ___ Standard 'end of letter' phrase
- ___ Asking about the times of classes on offer

WRITING PRACTICE

A PLAN Read the ad and write three or four questions you might ask.

Two-day professional interview course.

Learn how to be the perfect interview candidate.

Courses run by our company experts.

For more information, contact Ms. Petra Nagy at
p.nagy@professionaltraining.org

B PREPARE Organize your questions into a plan for a formal email.

C WRITE Write your email. Use your plan to help you.

VOCABULARY
Rooms and furniture

A Label pictures (1–10) with the words in the box.

armchair bathtub bed oven fridge lamp shower couch toilet dishwasher

1 ______________

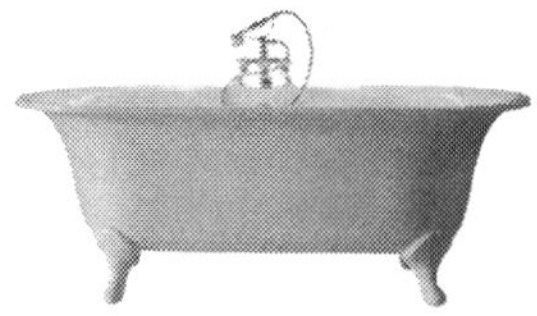

2 ______________

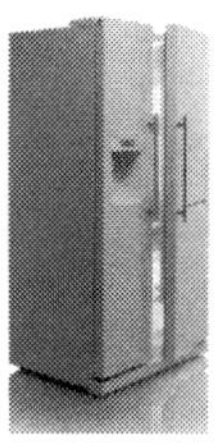

3 ______________

4 ______________

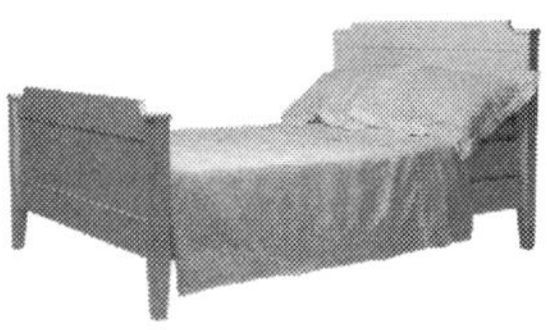

5 ______________

6 ______________

7 ______________

8 ______________

9 ______________

10 ______________

B Complete the table with the words from Exercise A.

Bedroom	Bathroom	Kitchen	Living room

PRONUNCIATION
/b/, /d/ and /g/

5.1 Listen and circle the word you hear.

1 bad dad
2 glue blue
3 dig big
4 gate date
5 boat goat
6 dot got

GRAMMAR
there is / are

A Choose the correct options to complete the conversation.

Beth: This house is so strange. There [1]*is / are* a couch in the bedroom, but there [2]*isn't / aren't* one in the living room.

Simon: Yes! It's weird. There [3]*isn't / aren't* any chairs in the living room either.

Beth: [4]*Is / Are* there a coffee machine in the kitchen?

Simon: Yes! There [5]*is / are* two! And there are [6]*any / some* plants.

Beth: Plants in the kitchen! Are there [7]*any / some* plants in the other rooms?

Simon: No, there aren't [8]*any / some* plants in the other rooms.

Beth: OK … this is strange. There [9]*is / are* a fridge in the living room.

Simon: A fridge?

Beth: Yes, and there [10]*is / are* two lamps next to it.

B Complete the paragraph with *there is*, *there isn't*, *there are* and *there aren't*.

Day 14 of 30:
My favorite room

JENNA THOMPSON | August 14, 2018 | 128 COMMENTS

My favorite room in my apartment is the living room. [1] ______________ two comfortable chairs and [2] ______________ a big couch. [3] ______________ a table because the room is too small, but [4] ______________ some lamps. [5] ______________ a TV across from the couch and [6] ______________ some books on a bookshelf. [7] ______________ any plants in the living room, but we have some in the kitchen.

VOCABULARY
Places in a town or city

A Complete the definitions with the places in the box.

~~café~~ gym library movie theater museum park subway station supermarket

1 *café* a place where you can buy tea, coffee and cake
2 ______ a large area with grass and trees
3 ______ a place where you can watch movies
4 ______ a place where you can look at or borrow books
5 ______ a place where you can catch a train
6 ______ a large store that sells food
7 ______ a place where you can exercise
8 ______ a place where you can see old, important objects

B Label the pictures with the words in the box.

airport hospital market restaurant stores theater

______

2 ______

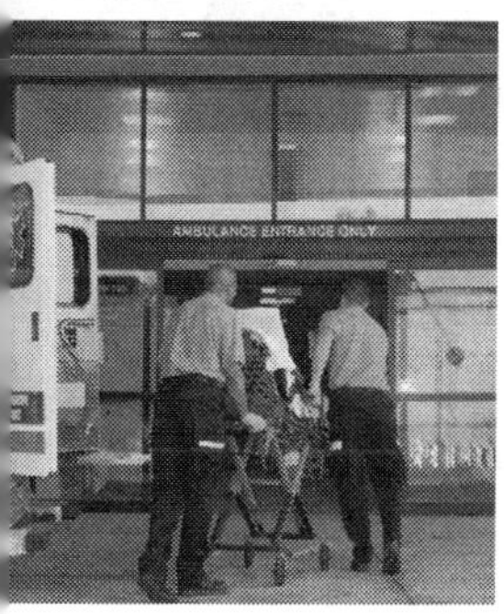

______

4 ______

______

6 ______

GRAMMAR
can

A Look at the pictures. Write sentences using the correct form of *can* and the words in parentheses.

(Lizzie / speak / Spanish)

1 ______

(he / ride / a bike)

2 ______

(she / sing)

3 ______

(he / swim)

4 ______

(he / make / sushi)

5 ______

(Sarah / play / violin)

6 ______

B Are these sentences correct or incorrect? Correct the mistakes.

1 We go can't to the movie theater tonight because it's closed.
2 It's amazing that you can't swim! Can your sister swim?
3 David can to speak three languages, English, French and Korean. His mom is French and his dad is South Korean.
4 I'm sorry! You can't borrow this book from the library. You can read it here.
5 She lives close to her office so she can walks to work in the morning.
6 I play guitar and I'm in a band. Do you can play a musical instrument?

PRONUNCIATION
Weak forms: *can/can't*

5.2 Listen to the sentences. Is the pronunciation of *can / can't* strong or weak?

1 Can you speak another language? *strong / weak*
2 Yes, I can. *strong / weak*
3 Can Danny speak Chinese well? *strong / weak*
4 No, he can't. *strong / weak*
5 But he can speak Japanese very well. *strong / weak*
6 Emily can't speak any other languages. *strong / weak*
7 Can they both speak French and Italian? *strong / weak*
8 Yes, they can. *strong / weak*

GRAMMAR
Imperatives

A Match situations (1–5) with imperatives (a–e).

1 ___ You are at the movie theater. The person in front of you is making a lot of noise.

2 ___ You are visiting a museum and want more information from the guide.

3 ___ You don't know how to use the coffee machine. Your friend is with you.

4 ___ Someone is running by the swimming pool. There is a no running sign next to them.

5 ___ You are with a friend. You see something amazing, but your friend isn't looking.

a Look at that!

b Please be quiet.

c Please don't run.

d Please help me.

e Tell me more.

B Complete the sentences with the verbs in the box.

be buy go listen push take touch turn

1 ______________ the lights off when you leave.

2 ______________ to this – an octopus has three hearts!

3 Elliott, don't ______________ your sister!

4 Turn left, then ______________ straight until the end of the road.

5 Please ______________ your shoes off at the door.

6 ______________ a travel guide before you go.

7 Don't ______________ anything children. It's all very expensive.

8 Sit down and ______________ quiet!

VOCABULARY
Adjectives to describe the appearance of things

Complete the descriptions with *a*, *e*, *i*, *o* or *u*.

The Hayward Gallery is a [1]**m__d__rn** building in London. A lot of people think it looks [2]**t__rr__bl__**. They say it's [3]**__gly** and should be knocked down!

The Sydney Opera House is an [4]**__m__z__ng** building. It looks [5]**b____t__f__l** with the [6]**str__ng__** shape of its roof. Some people think it looks like a sailing ship.

PRONUNCIATION
Word stress: adjectives

5.3 Listen and circle the adjective with a different stress pattern in each group.

1 big	(boring)	old
2 modern	ugly	beautiful
3 friendly	amazing	terrible
4 small	cool	ugly
5 interesting	modern	funny
6 popular	terrible	strange

Apartments and houses to rent

Stunning three-bedroom house

a House to rent with three bedrooms, a kitchen, living room, bathroom (no bathtub), a garage and a small yard. The rent is $2,100 per month. The house is close to some stores and there is a gym and a library just a five-minute walk from the house.

Modern studio apartment

b A studio apartment. One bedroom, fully equipped kitchen and living space with couch and table. There is a shower and a shared utility room with washing machine and dryer. It is ten minutes by bus to the city center from the apartment. The rent is $1,350 per month.

Four single rooms available

c Four individual rooms for rent in a large house. These are suitable for students or young professionals. There is a shared kitchen, bathroom and living room. All the bedrooms have locks. $700 + utility bills (water, electricity, internet) per person.

Two-bedroom apartment in a central location

d A modern, two-bedroom apartment in a great location across from a beautiful park and close to restaurants, a supermarket and five minutes from a subway station. From the station it is just 30 minutes by train to the city center. There is also on-street parking for a car. This is a perfect apartment for a young family.

Glossary

studio apartment (n) a small apartment that only has one main room

READING

A READ FOR SPECIFIC INFORMATION Read the ad. Which ad (a–d) matches the floorplan?

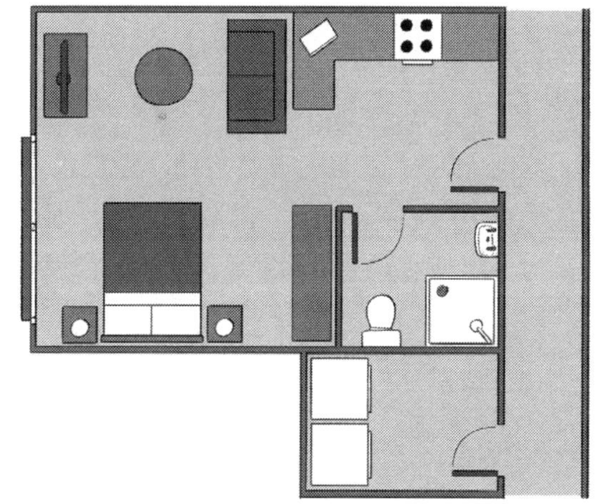

B READ FOR SPECIFIC INFORMATION Read the ad again. Check the correct ad(s) for each question.

	a	b	c	d
1 Which place has two bedrooms?				
2 Which place is just ten minutes away from the city center?				
3 Which place doesn't say how much the rent is?				
4 Which two places have stores nearby?				
5 In which place do you pay extra for electricity?				
6 Which two places have information about a place to park a car?				
7 Which place is not good for more than one or two people?				
8 In which two places do you share rooms with other people?				

C READ FOR DETAIL Read the ad again. Complete the sentences with no more than three words from the ad.

1. The three-bedroom house costs ________ a month.
2. It's a five-minute walk from a library and a ________.
3. In the studio apartment, there's a ________ and a dryer in the utility room.
4. The apartment is a ten-minute ________ trip from the city center.
5. Each room in the four-bedroom house has a ________ on the door.
6. Rent doesn't include utility ________ (water, electricity and internet).
7. The two-bedroom apartment is five minutes away from a ________.
8. It doesn't come with a garage, but there is ________ parking.

D REFLECT How would you describe where you live in an ad?

LISTENING

5.4 **A LISTEN FOR KEY WORDS** Listen to a conversation about neighborhoods. Check (✓) the topics that are discussed.

- ☐ places to eat
- ☐ local sports clubs
- ☐ street art
- ☐ tourism
- ☐ markets
- ☐ transportation in the city
- ☐ shopping centers
- ☐ parks and green spaces

Glossary

fashionable (adj) popular at a specific time

5.4 **B LISTEN FOR DETAIL** Listen again. Are these sentences true (T) or false (F)? Correct the false sentences.

1 Hannah thinks Camden market is amazing. *T / F*
2 There aren't any nice restaurants in Camden. *T / F*
3 Camden is very busy on the weekend. *T / F*
4 Victor lives in France. *T / F*
5 There is a park close to where Victor lives. *T / F*
6 There isn't any street art in Montreal. *T / F*
7 There aren't any old buildings in Montreal. *T / F*
8 Both Montreal and Camden are popular with tourists. *T / F*

C REFLECT Discuss the questions.

1 How do these two places compare to where you live?
2 How would you describe where you live? What's it like?

FUNCTIONAL LANGUAGE

Asking for and giving directions

A Match the beginnings of the sentences (1–6) with the ends of the sentences (a–f).

1 Go straight	a the café.
2 Turn	b of the road.
3 Go to the end	c ahead.
4 Go past	d turn on the right.
5 Take the second	e to the movie theater.
6 My apartment is next	f left.

B Put the conversation in the correct order.

☐ **Victor:** Movie theater on the right …
☐ **Hannah:** OK. Come out of the subway station. There is a bank across from the entrance.
☐ **Victor:** First turn on the right …
2 **Hannah:** Oh, hey Victor! Do you need directions to my apartment?
1 **Victor:** Hi Hannah! I'm at the subway station.
☐ **Hannah:** No, on the left. Walk to the end of the road. My apartment is on the left next to the café.
☐ **Victor:** … across from the subway station.
☐ **Hannah:** Walk past the movie theater. It's on the left.
☐ **Victor:** Yes, please.
☐ **Hannah:** Cross over the road and turn left. Then take the first turn on the right.

5.5 **C** Listen and check your answers to Exercise B.

1

2

3

WRITING

A Read *Paro Taktsang: The Tiger's Nest*. Match the description to the correct picture (1–3).

Paro Taktsang: The Tiger's Nest

A beautiful building in the mountains of Bhutan

Paro Taktsang, or the Tiger's Nest, is a famous building in Bhutan near northern India. The building is high up on the side of a mountain. There are amazing views across the valley below. The old building has white walls, and beautiful red and gold roofs that you can see from far away.

Paro Taktsang has eight main buildings that are all old caves. Inside the buildings you can see lots of paintings and some statues. You can't take photos inside the building, but you can take photos outside.

There is a long walk to reach Paro Taktsang. It takes around five hours to get there and back. The walk is interesting with lots of things to see. About halfway up there is a beautiful waterfall. There are not a lot of tourists at Paro Taktsang, so it is nice and quiet and it is a great place to visit.

B Read the article again and circle the adjectives.

C Write questions for these answers.

1 *What is the building called?*
Paro Taktsang.

2 ______
In Bhutan.

3 ______
It's a beautiful building with white walls and red and gold roofs.

4 ______
You can see paintings inside and visit a beautiful waterfall.

5 ______
It is nice and quiet and a great place to visit.

WRITING PRACTICE

A PLAN Choose a famous building and write notes about the following:

- what it's called
- where it is
- what it looks like
- what you can see or do there
- your opinion

B PREPARE Organize your notes into paragraphs. Try to add extra information.

C WRITE Use your plan to write a short description. Remember to use adjectives to make your writing more interesting.

6.1 That's Entertainment

Let's go out

VOCABULARY
Entertainment

A Label pictures (1–6) with the words in the box.

movie theater comedy show concert exhibit festival theater

1 ________________

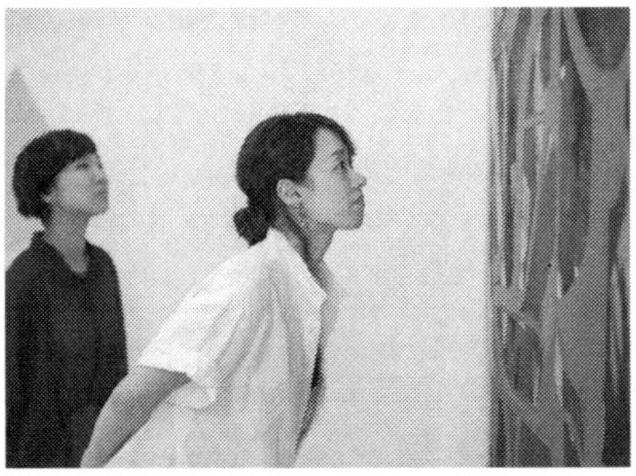

2 ________________

3 ________________

4 ________________

5 ________________

6 ________________

B Complete the sentences with the words from Exercise A.

1 There's a new art ____________ on at the Tate Modern. Do you want to go with me?

2 My parents try to go to the ____________ once a month to see plays like *Macbeth* and *Romeo and Juliet*.

3 Every Friday, we go to our local ____________ to watch a movie. The tickets are half price, so it's a great evening out!

4 My favorite ____________ is *Secret Solstice* in Iceland. Lots of amazing bands play there every year.

5 Busy week? Need a laugh? Come to our weekly ____________ with some of the best comedians around.

6 We have two tickets for a ____________ with the Beijing Orchestra. I'm really excited about it.

PRONUNCIATION
Word stress: noun patterns

6.1 Listen and circle the correct stress pattern.

1	concert	(Oo) / oO
2	music	Oo / oO
3	photograph	Ooo / oOo
4	entertainment	Oooo / ooOo
5	movie	Oo / oO
6	costume	Oo / oO

GRAMMAR
Likes and dislikes

A Correct the mistakes in each sentence.

1 I don't like stay in all the time!

2 I loves go to the movie theater.

3 They loves to playing soccer.

4 He not like watch TV.

5 I hates pizza!

6 We not like visit museums.

B Look at the table. Write six sentences about Ahmad with *love*, *like*, *don't like* or *hate* and a verb.

☺ ☺	soccer on TV / festivals
☺	Italian food
☹	video games
☹ ☹	theater / pop music

1 *Ahmad loves watching soccer on TV.*

2 Ahmad ____________________.

3 He ____________________.

4 ____________________.

5 ____________________.

6 ____________________.

GRAMMAR
was/were

A Reorder the words to make sentences and questions.

1 your / where / born / were / parents / ?

______

2 busy / this / my / really / train / morning / was

______

3 was / Tokyo / month / in / I / business / for / last

______

4 expensive / tickets / really / were / the / !

______

5 last / concert / was / how / the / night / ?

______

6 terrible / was / really / movie / a / that / !

______

7 week / it / hot / really / last / all / was

______

B Complete the conversation with *was, were, wasn't* and *weren't.*

Mike: That [1] ___*was*___ great. You know I love great comedy.

Alan: Well, the first two comedians [2] ______ very funny, but the third one [3] ______.

Mike: No, that's true. She [4] ______ terrible; the people in the club [5] ______ laughing at all.

Alan: I guess she [6] ______ brave to stand up there and keep going.

Mike: No, that [7] ______ stupid.

Alan: That [8] ______ a nice thing to say. I'm sure all the comedians [9] ______ trying their best.

Mike: I know, but it [10] ______ fairly expensive to get in.

Alan: True, but we [11] ______ there for three hours so it [12] ______ too bad.

PRONUNCIATION
Weak forms: *was/were*

6.2 Listen and choose the correct pronunciation of *was* and *were.*

1	That was a really great concert.	/wəz/	/wʌz/
2	Yes, it was.	/wəz/	/wʌz/
3	Were there lots of people?	/wər/	/wɜːr/
4	Yes, there were.	/wər/	/wɜːr/
5	Were your friends at the concert?	/wər/	/wɜːr/
6	Yes, they were.	/wər/	/wɜːr/
7	It was fairly expensive.	/wəz/	/wʌz/
8	Yes, it was really expensive.	/wəz/	/wʌz/

VOCABULARY
Past time expressions

A Complete the paragraph with *in, ago* or *last.*

This is a picture of my aunt, the famous Japanese actress, Fumi Watanabe. She was born [1] ______ 1978 and appeared in her first movie [2] ______ 1986 at the age of just 8. Two years [3] ______, she won an award for her acting and she was very proud. [4] ______ month she was nominated again and she hopes to win for a second time. The awards take place [5] ______ the winter and it is always really cold. She called me twenty minutes [6] ______ to tell me she has tickets to the event for the whole family. I'm so excited.

B Are the sentences correct or incorrect? Correct the incorrect ones.

1 The first Oscar ceremony was last 1929.

2 They were at the movie theater in night.

3 Were you at home last weekend?

4 There was a concert two nights ago.

5 Peter was at college five years last.

6 There's a great music festival here in July.

GRAMMAR
Simple past regular and irregular verbs

A **Complete the paragraph with the correct form of the verbs in the box.**

be	begin	die	make	move
reach	release	start	win	work

David Bowie [1] ______ born in London on January 8, 1947. At the age of 13, he [2] ______ to learn the saxophone. In 1969, the song *Space Oddity* [3] ______ number 5 in the UK music charts. Six years later, Bowie [4] ______ to Los Angeles and [5] ______ his movie career with a performance in the movie *The Man Who Fell to Earth*. Over the next few years, Bowie [6] ______ on a number of different projects and in 1979 [7] ______ his first theater performance on Broadway. Over his 50-year career, Bowie [8] ______ six Grammys for his music and 25 awards in total. In January 2016, Bowie [9] ______ at the age of 69 just two days after he [10] ______ his last album, *Blackstar*.

B **Complete the sentences with the simple past form of the verb in parentheses.**

1 We ______ (*take*) lots of photos on our trip to Hawaii.
2 I ______ (*go*) to see the new *Star Wars* movie at the Roxy last night.
3 Paolo ______ (*move*) to Los Angeles last year to become an actor.
4 My father ______ (*buy*) me a new camera for my birthday.
5 I ______ (*see*) a great comedian on TV last night, but I can't remember her name!
6 The *Bergen International Film Festival* in Norway ______ (*start*) in 2000.
7 Junko ______ (*meet*) her husband five years ago.
8 Leonardo DiCaprio ______ (*win*) an Oscar for Best Actor in 2016.

PRONUNCIATION
Simple past regular endings

6.3 **Listen to the simple past verbs. Is the final sound /d/, /t/ or /ɪd/? Circle the correct sounds.**

1 hated	/d/ /t/ /ɪd/
2 helped	/d/ /t/ /ɪd/
3 looked	/d/ /t/ /ɪd/
4 married	/d/ /t/ /ɪd/
5 performed	/d/ /t/ /ɪd/
6 played	/d/ /t/ /ɪd/
7 practiced	/d/ /t/ /ɪd/
8 started	/d/ /t/ /ɪd/

VOCABULARY
Life events

Complete the life events (1–8) with the verbs in the box.

became	got	had	moved
started	studied	was	went

1 Ella ______ to Oxford University where she met Mark.

2 Mark and Ella both ______ languages at the university.

3 Mark ______ work as a journalist after attending the university.

4 Ella ______ a famous actress after attending the university.

5 Mark and Ella ______ married in the summer of 2002.

6 They ______ to a new house in 2004.

7 Their son, Jacob, ______ born the following year.

8 Mark and Ella ______ three children, Jacob, James and Jack.

THIS WEEK AT THE MOVIES

JORDAN STEVENS | May 4, 2018 | 899 COMMENTS

3200 (PG-13)

This movie is set in the future and the story is about the lives of a boy and his sister. I usually don't like this type of movie, but the two young actors, Damian Shultz and Greta Simons, were amazing as the boy and girl. The story is good and you don't know what is going to happen next and this keeps you interested the whole time. This is a movie to go and see in the movie theater.

Laugh Night (PG-13)

I love to laugh, so I was very excited when I went to the movie theater. In the end, I wasn't happy. I saw the trailer and thought the movie looked great. I knew one of the actors, Tosh Ellis, and liked his last two movies, but he wasn't good in this one. I think I laughed twice in the 90 minutes, not very good when a ticket costs $8. Watch the trailer, but not the movie, as that's about as good as it gets!

The Blade (NC-17)

One of the best movies of the year, but that isn't a surprise. Emma Davies won an Oscar last year and was great in this movie. The director, Ivan Rodriguez, is excellent and I love all his movies! I also loved the special effects. It's the type of horror movie people will love or hate, but that's always the way with this genre. The only problem was the end wasn't very good, but I thought the movie was awesome!

Glossary

director (n) the person who tells the actors what to do when they make a movie
genre (n) a type of book, movie or music
special effects (n) the sounds and images in a movie made with technology, for example with computers
trailer (n) an ad for a movie or a TV show that shows a small part of the movie or show

READING

A READ FOR GIST Read the movie reviews. Then match the name of a movie with a summary of the writer's opinion (1–3).

1 A funny trailer, but a bad movie. ________
2 Another movie from a great director. ________
3 A good movie to see at the movie theater. ________

B READ FOR DETAIL Read the reviews again. Are these sentences true (T) or false (F)? Correct the false sentences.

1 The writer thought the acting in *3200* was good. T/F
2 The writer doesn't recommend *3200*. T/F
3 The writer usually likes movies that make him laugh. T/F
4 The writer thought *Laugh Night* was funny. T/F
5 The writer was surprised that *The Blade* was so good. T/F
6 The writer thinks that not everyone likes horror movies. T/F

C SCAN Scan the reviews again. Complete the sentences with names from the text.

1 ________ won an Oscar for a different movie.
2 ________ and ________ are both young actors.
3 The writer loves movies directed by ________.
4 The writer liked other movies that ________ was in.

D REFLECT Answer the questions.

1 What was the last movie you saw at the movie theater?
2 What was the movie about?
3 Did you enjoy it? Why/Why not?
4 Which of the three movies (*3200*, *Laugh Night*, *The Blade*) would you like to see? Why?

LISTENING

A LISTEN FOR KEY WORDS Listen to a conversation about a movie. Number the topics in the order they are discussed. 6.4

- ☐ The actors
- ☐ The director
- ☐ The music
- ☐ The special effects

B LISTEN FOR DETAIL Listen again and answer the questions. 6.4

1 What did Silvia think of the actors?
 a They were awful. **b** They were great. **c** She isn't sure.

2 What does Luke describe as awesome?
 a the actors **b** the special effects **c** the story

3 Who does Meryl Adams play in the movie?
 a the mother **b** the sister **c** the daughter

4 What did Rick think was awful?
 a the director **b** the music **c** the special effects

5 Who or what does Luke describe as amazing?
 a Meryl Adams **b** the music **c** the director

6 Who doesn't think the director could win an Oscar for this movie?
 a Rick **b** Luke **c** Silvia

C REFLECT How do you choose the movies you watch?

FUNCTIONAL LANGUAGE

Asking for and giving opinions

Complete the conversation with the words in the box. Then listen again and check. 6.4

about awesome awful ~~great~~ hate loved OK sure think

Luke: So what did you think of the movie?
Silvia: Honestly, Luke. It wasn't [1] *great*.
Luke: Really? I [2] ______ it! I thought the actors were great.
Silvia: What do you mean? I thought they were [3] ______.
Luke: That's not true. How [4] ______ you, Rick?
Rick: I'm not [5] ______.
Luke: What? Come on. The special effects were [6] ______!
Rick: Yes, that's true, but you also need good actors and an interesting story.
Luke: I loved the actors. Meryl Adams was great as the mother.
Silvia: That's true, but the other actors were terrible.
Luke: Rick, what do you [7] ______?
Rick: Uh, some of the acting was [8] ______, but generally I think I agree with Silvia … and the music was awful.
Luke: What? I love that type of music.
Rick: I know you do, but I [9] ______ it.
Luke: What about the director? He's amazing.
Rick: Hmm … I don't know. He hasn't won an Oscar, has he?
Luke: No, that's true, but he could win one for this movie.
Silvia: Ha ha! Now I know you're joking!

6.6 That's Entertainment

Write a review of an event

★★★★☆ 10 days ago

Day of the 'killer' tomato

Laura M

a I went to my first festival in Spain in 2010 and every year try to go to a new one somewhere in Europe. Last year, I went to the famous La Tomatina festival in Buñol near Valencia with three of my friends.

b We bought tickets for a three-day tour and we stayed in a hotel in Valencia. The ticket cost $175, but that included the hotel for three nights, so I think it was a fairly good value.

c Buñol is about 38 km from Valencia, so first we woke up early and drove to the town. We got to the Plaza del Pueblo in the center of the town at around 10 am. Next, at about 11 am, a water cannon was fired into the crowd. Then, people started picking up tomatoes and throwing them at each other. You have to squash the tomatoes in your hand before you throw them so they don't hurt anyone.

d The whole event lasted an hour. It finished when another water cannon was fired. After that, we tried to find somewhere to clean up. We were lucky as we found someone with a big hose. Finally, we found a café to have lunch and laugh about the day.

e I thought it was really fun – almost 20,000 people having a big fight with tomatoes! Next year I want to go to the Cheese Rolling in England.

WRITING

A Look at the picture. What do you think happens at the event?

B Read the review. Check your ideas from Exercise A.

C Read the review again. Are these sentences true (T) or false (F)? Correct the false sentences.

1. Laura went to the festival alone. *T / F*
2. The hotel cost $175 per night. *T / F*
3. They stayed in Buñol. *T / F*
4. The event started at 11 am. *T / F*
5. The event takes about three hours. *T / F*
6. She plans on going to a different festival next year. *T / F*

D Scan the review again. Match topics (1–5) with paragraphs (a–e).

1. Details of the event ___
2. The writer's opinion ___
3. Background ___
4. Cost of the event ___
5. How the event ends ___

E Scan the review again and <u>underline</u> the narrative sequencers (*then*, *after that*, etc).

F Put the events of the story in the correct order. Use the narrative sequencing words to help you.

___ Next, actors dressed in 1920s costumes showed us to our seats.

___ Finally, we watched the end of the movie. It was a great night.

___ First, we waited in the line to get into the venue.

___ After that, we had dinner while a live band played music from the movie.

___ Then, we watched the first half of the movie.

WRITING PRACTICE

A **PREPARE** Think of an event that you went to and write notes about the topics in Exercise D.

B **WRITE** Use your notes to write a review. Use narrative sequencers to organize your ideas.

Irregular Verbs

Base form	Simple past	Past participle
be	was/were	been
become	became	become
begin	began	begun
break	broke	broken
bring	brought	brought
build	built	built
buy	bought	bought
can	could	(been able to)
catch	caught	caught
choose	chose	chosen
come	came	come
cost	cost	cost
cut	cut	cut
do	did	done
drink	drank	drunk
eat	ate	eaten
fall	fell	fallen
feel	felt	felt
find	found	found
forget	forgot	forgotten
get	got	got
give	gave	given
go	went	gone/been
grow	grew	grown
have	had	had
hear	heard	heard
hit	hit	hit
hold	held	held
hurt	hurt	hurt
keep	kept	kept
know	knew	known
leave	left	left
lend	lent	lent

Base form	Simple past	Past participle
let	let	let
lose	lost	lost
make	made	made
mean	meant	meant
meet	met	met
must	had to	(had to)
pay	paid	paid
put	put	put
read	read	read
ride	rode	ridden
run	ran	run
say	said	said
see	saw	seen
sell	sold	sold
set	set	set
shut	shut	shut
sing	sang	sung
sit	sat	sat
sleep	slept	slept
speak	spoke	spoken
spell	spelled	spelled
spend	spent	spent
stand	stood	stood
steal	stole	stolen
take	took	taken
teach	taught	taught
tell	told	told
think	thought	thought
throw	threw	thrown
understand	understood	understood
wear	wore	worn
win	won	won
write	wrote	written

PHONETIC SYMBOLS

Single vowels

/ɪ/	f**i**sh	/fɪʃ/
/iː/	b**ea**n	/biːn/
/ʊ/	f**oo**t	/fʊt/
/uː/	sh**oe**	/ʃuː/
/e/	**e**gg	/eg/
/ə/	moth**er**	/ˈmʌðər/
/ɜː/	w**or**d	/wɜːrd/
/ɔː/	t**al**k	/tɔːk/
/æ/	b**a**ck	/bæk/
/ʌ/	b**u**s	/bʌs/
/ɑː/	**ar**m	/ɑːrm/
/ɒ/	t**o**p	/tɒp/

Diphthongs

/uw/	n**ew**	/nuw/
/eɪ/	f**a**ce	/feɪs/
/ɔɪ/	b**oy**	/bɔɪ/
/oʊ/	n**o**se	/noʊz/
/ju/	**u**se	/juz/
/aɪ/	**eye**	/aɪ/
/aʊ/	m**ou**th	/maʊθ/

Consonants

/p/	**p**en	/pen/	/s/	**s**nake	/sneɪk/
/b/	**b**ag	/bæg/	/z/	**z**oo	/zuː/
/t/	**t**ea	/tiː/	/ʃ/	**sh**op	/ʃɒp/
/d/	**d**og	/dɒg/	/ʒ/	televi**si**on	/ˈtelɪvɪʒən/
/ʧ/	**ch**ip	/ʧɪp/	/m/	**m**ap	/mæp/
/ʤ/	**j**azz	/ʤæz/	/n/	**n**ame	/neɪm/
/k/	**c**ake	/keɪk/	/ŋ/	ri**ng**	/rɪŋ/
/g/	**g**irl	/gɜːrl/	/h/	**h**ouse	/haʊs/
/f/	**f**ilm	/fɪlm/	/l/	**l**eg	/leg/
/v/	**v**erb	/vɜːrb/	/r/	**r**oad	/roʊd/
/θ/	**th**ing	/θɪŋ/	/w/	**w**ant	/wɒnt/
/ð/	**th**ese	/ðiːz/	/j/	**y**es	/jes/

UNIT 1

Lesson 1.5, Listening, Exercise A
1.4 **M = Mom Mx = Max**

M: Uh, hello?
Mx: Hi, Mom!
M: Hello?
Mx: Hello? Can you hear me?
M: Oh, hi Max. How are you?
Mx: I'm fine, thanks. How are you?
M: Not too bad. Your father's at the golf club today and your sister's at work, so it's nice and quiet at home. Where are you now?
Mx: I'm in Hanoi in Vietnam.
M: Really? Wow! What's it like there?
Mx: It's really, really hot and raining a lot.
M: Oh. But, you don't have your umbrella! You left it here.
Mx: Don't worry, Mom. I'm fine. I have a coat.
M: Oh, OK. Well, I hope you're eating well.
Mx: Of course I am.
M: Is the food good?
Mx: Yes, it's delicious.
M: Well, don't eat anything strange out there.
Mx: Ha ha! Strange? Like what?
M: Like . . . like . . . I don't know, insects or something!
Mx: Insects? Well some people do eat grasshoppers . . .
M: Grasshoppers? Max, you must come home!
Mx: Mom, relax. I'm fine. The food's fine. Everything is fine.
M: Hmm . . . OK. Well, what's your next destination?
Mx: Thailand, I think.
M: Do you need any money?
Mx: No, Mom. I have money. Say *Hi* to Dad for me.
M: OK. Bye, darling. Bye. I love you! Remember to . . . Max? Max?

Lesson 1.5, Functional Language
1.5 **Mx = Max E = Emily**

Mx: Excuse me, is this the train to Sapa?
E: Yes, it is.
Mx: Oh, great. Thanks. I'm Max by the way.
E: Nice to meet you Max. I'm Emily and this is my friend Sophie.
Mx: Nice to meet you both. How are you?
E: Not too bad. And you?
Mx: I'm fine, thanks.
E: So where are you from, Max?

UNIT 2

Lesson 2.5, Listening, Exercise A
2.4 **M = Maha J = Jess**

J: Hi Maha, sorry I'm late – I had to finish something at work.
M: Ha ha! Don't worry, you're here now. Sit down and relax.
J: All right. How are you, anyway? How was the wedding?
M: It was great. Would you like to see some photos?
J: Sure.
M: OK, hold on . . . Here you go. Here's a picture of the whole family.
J: Oh, wow! There's a lot of you. So, who's who?
M: The young man with the short dark hair is my brother, Hamad.
J: He looks very serious.
M: Ha ha! No, he's not. He's really funny and he makes everyone laugh.
J: And who's the slim woman with long black hair?
M: Do you mean the woman next to him?
J: Yes. Is that his wife?
M: No, that's our cousin, Fauzia.
J: And are those your parents?
M: Yes, my mother is the one with short gray hair and glasses and my father has a beard and a mustache.
J: Everyone looks so happy.
M: Of course! It's a wedding photo.
J: Oh, who's the woman with long blond hair and blue eyes?
M: Oh, that's Mandy. She's my brother's wife. She's American.
J: Well, it looks like an amazing day.
M: Yeah, it was great. Anyway, what do you want to drink?
J: Just a coffee, please. Milk, no sugar.
M: OK, I'll go and order for us.

Lesson 2.5, Functional Language
2.5 **M = Maha D = Doug**

D: Can I help you?
M: Yes, please. Could I have a coffee with milk and a green tea?
D: Of course. Anything to eat?
M: Could I have a chocolate cookie?
D: No, sorry. I'm afraid not. We don't have any left.
M: OK, no problem. How much is that?
D: That's $4.60.
M: Thanks.

UNIT 3

Lesson 3.5, Listening, Exercise A
3.5 **S = Simon B = Beth**

S: Hey, Beth – your birthday's this month, isn't it?
B: Ugh! Yes. It's on Saturday.
S: Ha ha! You don't sound very happy about it!
B: I'm old Simon!

S: What? You're 26! That's not old! Come on, let's do something to celebrate!

B: Why? It's not a special day.

S: Of course it's a special day! It's your birthday. We need to do something . . .

B: OK, OK. What do you want to do?

S: Let's have a party!

B: No, I don't want a party. I don't like big groups of people.

S: OK, but we have to celebrate. Why don't we go out to eat?

B: I'm not sure. I don't have a lot of money. Why don't we just cook something here?

S: No. It's a special occasion, so we need to do something special. How about going to see that new Tom Hanks movie?

B: Now, that's a great idea! I love Tom Hanks! What about Friday evening after work?

S: That sounds good. Hold on. Let me check what time it's showing. OK, there are two shows – one at 7:15 and one at 9:30.

B: 9:30 is too late. Let's go to the one at 7:15.

S: Awesome! I'll book the tickets for 7:15.

UNIT 4

Lesson 4.5, Listening, Exercise A

4.4 **I = Interviewer G = Graham**

I: Good morning. Can I ask you a few questions about your job?

G: OK, sure.

I: What do you do?

G: I'm an actor! Ha ha!

I: Really? Wow! Do you work on TV?

G: Um, not TV, no.

I: Oh, so movies then? Or the theater?

G: No, not movies or the theater.

I: But I thought you said you're an actor!

G: Well, I want to be an actor.

I: Oh, I see. So what do you do at the moment?

G: I work as a receptionist.

I: Oh! I see. Do you work in an office?

G: Yes, I do. My job is to answer the phones, take messages and greet visitors.

I: Do you work nine to five?

G: Yes, I do and I have an hour for lunch at noon.

I: Do you have to wear a uniform?

G: No, I don't.

I: And do you work for a big company?

G: Yes, it's a very big company. It has offices in 20 different countries.

I: Do you like your job?

G: No, I don't. It's really boring.

I: Do you want to change your job?

G: Not really. I want to move to the Los Angeles office.

I: Oh, to be near Hollywood . . .

G: Yes, I want to be a famous Hollywood actor.

I: Thank you, Graham. Next week . . .

Lesson 4.5, Functional Language

4.5 **R = Receptionist RK = Richard Kershaw**

R: Good morning. This is Schmidt and Brandt. Can I help you?

RK: Hello. Could I speak to Hannah Schmidt, please?

R: Who's speaking, please?

RK: It's Richard Kershaw.

R: Hold on a minute, please. I'm afraid she isn't available right now. Would you like to leave a message?

RK: Yes, please. Can you ask her to call Richard from S-REK Ltd at 800-555-0199, please?

R: I'm sorry, can you repeat that?

UNIT 5

Lesson 5.5, Listening, Exercise A

5.4 **V = Victor H = Hannah**

V: So where do you live, Hannah?

H: I live in Camden in north London.

V: Oh, hold on. Is there a really big market there?

H: Yes, that's right. It's amazing!

V: What sort of things can you buy there?

H: Anything, really. Clothes, food, jewelry . . . Yes, Camden is a fashionable place to live. There are a few amazing restaurants and some really good cafés.

V: Sounds great.

H: Yeah, some of the restaurants there are amazing, and most of the cafés are pretty good.

V: Is it busy?

H: Uh, yes. It gets really busy on the weekend because it's so popular with tourists. Apparently, around 100,000 people visit Camden every weekend!

V: Wow! Yeah, that is busy. Maybe I should go on Friday. I need to buy a few presents before I fly back on Sunday. Is it close to the station?

H: Yes, it's really easy. Just turn right out of the subway and walk straight up Camden High Street. The market is about a two-minute walk away. I'd go early though, as it gets really, really busy by lunchtime. Anyway, tell me about you. Where do you live?

V: I live in Montreal.

H: In Canada?

V: Yes, that's right. I work at a university there.

H: What's Montreal like?

V: I love it. I live in the center, but my apartment is right next to a park, so it doesn't feel like you're in a really big city.

H: Nice. So is it an interesting place to live?

V: Uh, yes. I think so. There are lots of museums and theaters. It is definitely not a boring place to live!

H: Is there anything strange in Montreal?

V: Strange? Well, there's a lot of graffiti and street art which some people don't like, but I think it's great.

H: Ha ha. What about the buildings. Are they all modern?

V: No, there are some beautiful old buildings. To be honest, the only real problem with the city is that it's so popular with tourists. It can get pretty noisy and crowded, especially on the weekend.

H: So Camden and Montreal are very similar . . .

V: Ha ha! Yeah, it sounds like it!

Lesson 5.5, Functional Language, Exercise C
5.5 **V = Victor H = Hannah**

V: Hi Hannah. I'm at the subway station.

H: Oh, hey Victor! Do you need directions to my apartment?

V: Yes, please.

H: OK. Come out of the subway station. There is a bank across from the entrance.

V: . . . across from the subway station.

H: Cross over the road and turn left. Then take the first turn on the right.

V: First turn on the right . . .

H: Walk past the movie theater. It's on the left.

V: Movie theater on the right . . .

H: No, on the left. Walk to the end of the road. My apartment is on the left next to the café.

UNIT 6

Lesson 6.5, Listening, Exercise A
6.4 **R = Rick L = Luke S = Silvia**

L: So what did you think of the movie?

S: Honestly, Luke. It wasn't great.

L: Really? I loved it! I thought the actors were great.

S: What do you mean? I thought they were awful.

L: That's not true. How about you, Rick?

R: I'm not sure.

L: What? Come on. The special effects were awesome!

R: Yes, that's true, but you also need good actors and an interesting story.

L: I loved the actors. Meryl Adams was great as the mother.

S: That's true, but the other actors were terrible.

L: Rick, what do you think?

R: Uh, some of the acting was OK, but generally I think I agree with Silvia . . . and the music was awful.

L: What? I love that type of music.

R: I know you do, but I hate it.

L: What about the director? He's amazing.

R: Hmm . . . I don't know. He hasn't won an Oscar, has he?

L: No, that's true but he could win one for this movie.

S: Ha ha! Now I know you're joking!

Answer key

1.1 People and places

VOCABULARY

A
1 Canada **2** US **3** Mexico **4** Brazil **5** Spain **6** France
7 Turkey **8** India **9** China **10** Japan

B
1 Canada **2** Canadian **3** Japanese **4** Mexico
5 Mexican **6** Chinese **7** China **8** British
9 Sweden **10** Swedish

PRONUNCIATION

Oo	oO	Ooo	ooO	oOoo
British Polish	Brazil Japan	Mexican	Japanese Vietnam	Canadian Colombia

GRAMMAR

A
1 'm **2** 're **3** is **4** 'm not **5** aren't **6** isn't

B
1 'm/am **2** is **3** 'm/am **4** isn't / is not **5** 's / is
6 're / are **7** is **8** 're / are **9** aren't / are not **10** 're / are
11 's / is **12** 'm / am **13** 'm not / am not **14** 'm / am
15 're / are

1.2 Where are you?

VOCABULARY

A
2 25,312 **3** 9,730 **4** 2,500,000 **5** 18,880 **6** 316

B
1 e **2** b **3** d **4** a **5** c

PRONUNCIATION
1 30 **2** 14 **3** 60 **4** 15 **5** 13 **6** 18

GRAMMAR

A
2 Tell me about the city. ~~It is~~ **Is it** expensive?
3 ~~Is~~ **Are** your parents Japanese?
4 Hi, Erin! How **are you**?
5 **Is it** hot there?
6 What**'s** your favorite type of food?
7 Oh, really? Where **are you** now?
8 **Are you** ~~is~~ busy?

B
2 Are you Spanish?
3 How far is Seoul from Paris?
4 Where are you now?
5 What's your favorite food?

1.3 What's in your bag?

VOCABULARY
1 headphones
2 umbrella
3 money
4 laptop
5 watch
6 wallet
7 tissues
8 keys
9 magazine
10 cell phone
11 bottle of water
12 credit card

GRAMMAR

A
1 an **2** an **3** a **4** – **5** an **6** a **7** – **8** a

B
1 that **2** those **3** this **4** these **5** these **6** that

PRONUNCIATION
2 book **3** wallet **4** it **5** watch **6** tissues

1.4 Reading

READING

A
1 Elsa **2** Sandra **3** Ralph **4** Greg

B
1 cold **2** headphones **3** credit card **4** work **5** baby
6 a newspaper **7** everything **8** have food

1.5 Listening; Functional Language

LISTENING

A
1 a **2** b **3** c **4** c

B
1 T
2 F (It's really, really hot and raining a lot.)
3 F (Max says it's delicious.)
4 T
5 T
6 F (He says he has money.)

FUNCTIONAL LANGUAGE
1 I'm **2** meet **3** this **4** How **5** too **6** fine

1.6 Fill in a form with personal details

WRITING

A
1 c **2** b **3** a

B
1 First **2** Last **3** Home **4** Phone **5** Email
6 Occupation **7** Type **8** Number **9** Payment
10 Duration

C
1 Jemma **2** Khan **3** Chinese **4** Shanghai **5** China

WRITING PRACTICE

Model answer

Registration form for English classes.
First name: Julian **Nationality:** French
Last name: Duchamp **Email:** jd123@languageschool.fr
Date of birth: 12/08/1994 **Phone number:** 555 124552
Duration of course: 3 weeks ☐ 6 weeks ☐ 12 weeks ☑
Payment type: Cash ☐ Debit card ☑ Credit card ☐

2.1 Family

VOCABULARY

2 mother **3** husband **4** grandmother **5** uncle
6 cousins **7** grandfather **8** parents **9** sister **10** wife
11 aunt **12** children **13** father

PRONUNCIATION

1 cousin **2** famous **3** husband **4** curious **5** actress
6 celebrate **7** family **8** again

GRAMMAR

A

1 my **2** her **3** our **4** Their **5** His **6** Its

B

1 parents' **2** sister's **3** wife's **4** grandparents'
5 children's **6** David's **7** James's **8** weeks'

2.2 The same, but different

VOCABULARY

A

1 d **2** c **3** e **4** f **5** a **6** b

B

Hair length	Hair type	Hair color	Other
long	bald	blond	beard
short	curly	brown	glasses
	straight	gray	mustache

GRAMMAR

A

1 have **2** Does **3** has **4** don't have
5 have **6** doesn't have **7** Does **8** have

B

1 My uncle has a Ferrari.
2 Amy and Tim don't have any children.
3 Does your mother have blue eyes?
4 He doesn't have a famous cousin.
5 Both of my sisters have blond hair.
6 Danielle's sister doesn't have her sunglasses today.
7 I have a car, but my brother doesn't.
8 We don't have time to go to the store.

PRONUNCIATION

1 She has **2** We have **3** I have **4** She has
5 he has **6** you have **7** She has **8** we have

2.3 Friends

VOCABULARY

A

1 messy **2** noisy **3** serious **4** friendly **5** quiet

B

1 c **2** a **3** a **4** c **5** b **6** c **7** c

PRONUNCIATION

●	●•	●••	•●•
blond	curly	serious	unfriendly
neat	different		unhappy
straight	quiet		
tall			

GRAMMAR

A

1 Tristan is a fairly serious person.
2 Your roommates are very friendly.
3 My sister's bedroom is really messy.
4 Are your neighbors very noisy?
5 The office is very quiet this morning.
6 Is your new apartment expensive?

B

1 My boss isn't a very friend**ly** person. He is always shouting.
2 What happened? You're usually **fairly** neat ~~fairly~~.
3 Your children are both really tall~~s~~.
4 My best friend is ~~a~~ very funny. He's always telling jokes.
5 Your parents never smile. They're **really** serious people ~~really~~.
6 Are you OK? You're **fairly** quiet ~~fairly~~ today.

2.4 Reading

READING

A

1

B

1 F (Mona De Luca lives with a younger brother and sister.)
2 T
3 F (Mona's father is named Ralph.)
4 F (Ralph's children say he is serious and never laughs or smiles.)
5 F (Mona's grandmother is 79 years old.)
6 T

C

1 d **2** a **3** c **4** e **5** b

2.5 Listening; Functional Language

LISTENING

A

her brother, her cousin, her parents, her brother's wife

B

1 c **2** e **3** d **4** b **5** a

FUNCTIONAL LANGUAGE

2 please **3** course **4** Could **5** sorry **6** not
7 problem **8** that **9** dollars

2.6 Write an email to a friend

WRITING

A

who they live with, what they study,
who is in their class

B

1 T
2 T
3 F (Next year, we have to choose chemistry or biology.)
4 F (Emma doesn't live near the university. It's about 30 minutes away.)
5 T
6 F (Sophie is one of her classmates.)
7 F (Carlos is Emma's roommate.)
8 T

C

1 and **2** but **3** and **4** or **5** or **6** and **7** but
8 and **9** and

WRITING PRACTICE

B

Model answer

Hi Francesco,
It was good to hear from you. I'm very well, thanks. How are you? Are you still going to college?
I'm now working at an advertising company in the center of the city. I'm really enjoying it. The people I work with are very friendly. My boss is also very helpful and she has taught me a lot of new skills.
I'm still living in the same apartment as before. My roommate can be annoying sometimes – he is so messy. He also watches TV late at night, which keeps me awake. I will look for a new place to live next month. Maybe I can find an apartment closer to the office.
Best wishes,
Gianni

3.1 A typical day

VOCABULARY

A

1 get up **2** leave **3** get **4** have **5** have
6 go **7** take **8** read **9** watch **10** go

B

1 d **2** e **3** a **4** c **5** b

GRAMMAR

A

1 live **2** watches **3** listen **4** works **5** has **6** go

B

1 lives **2** get up **3** have **4** works **5** likes
6 teaches **7** go **8** writes

PRONUNCIATION

A

/s/	/z/	/ɪz/
starts	goes	teaches
writes	has	watches
	lives	

B

2 takes **3** works **4** watches **5** writes

3.2 All day, every day

GRAMMAR

A

1 I usually sleep for eight hours a night.
2 Milos and Ali / Ali and Milos are always late for class.
3 Samantha always has three cups of coffee in the morning.
4 My brother sometimes plays soccer on the weekend.
5 It is never really cold in Thailand.
6 I often play video games in the evening.

B

2 Emily never takes a shower in the morning.
3 Emily rarely plays video games on the weekend.
4 Emily always goes to yoga classes.
5 Ben always listens to music on the way to work.
6 Ben usually takes a shower in the morning.
7 Ben sometimes plays video games on the weekend.
8 Ben rarely goes to yoga classes.

PRONUNCIATION

Oo	oO	Ooo	oOo
coffee	Japan	exercise	director
weekend		interesting	umbrella
yoga		radio	

VOCABULARY

A

1 in **2** on **3** on **4** at **5** On **6** in

B

1 My boss usually has meetings **in** the afternoon.
2 I never use my phone **at** night.
3 correct
4 Georgina sometimes goes for a run **on** Saturdays.
5 correct
6 correct

3.3 A special day

GRAMMAR

A

1 don't live **2** don't see **3** doesn't come **4** doesn't enjoy
5 doesn't like **6** doesn't make **7** don't eat

B

1 correct
2 My father **doesn't** ~~don't~~ like science fiction movies.
3 She **doesn't** ~~no~~ listen to music at work.
4 correct
5 I **don't** ~~not~~ speak Spanish very well.

VOCABULARY

Down

2 fireworks **4** party

Across

3 special **5** parades **6** presents **7** decorations

PRONUNCIATION

1 We always have a party on the 4th of July.
2 They don't put up decorations until December.
3 We open our presents in the morning.
4 There's a big parade in November.
5 My mother always makes traditional food.
6 Brad doesn't celebrate his birthday.

3.4 Reading

A

1

B

2 wash up **3** have breakfast **4** call mission control
5 have lunch **6** repair equipment **7** exercise

C

1 T
2 F (After getting up, he always washes up. There isn't a shower.)
3 T
4 F (In the past, food came out of tubes, but now they eat a lot of the same food they did on Earth.)
5 F (He says it's 'boring'.)
6 F (Astronauts usually exercise for two hours a day.)
7 T

3.5 Listening; Functional Language

LISTENING

A

have a party, go out to eat, watch a movie

B

1 Saturday **2** twenty-six / 26 **3** special **4** big groups
5 money **6** Friday evening **7** seven fifteen / 7:15
8 book the tickets

FUNCTIONAL LANGUAGE

A

1 Why **2** How **3** about **4** Let's
a Awesome **b** sure **c** sounds **d** great

B

1 b **2** d **3** c **4** a

3.6 Write a blog post about your day

WRITING

A

1

B

1 c **2** b **3** c **4** c **5** c **6** b **7** b

C

Before, After that, After breakfast, Then, Finally

D

1 get up
2 have a cup of coffee
3 take a shower
4 get dressed
5 check schedule
6 have breakfast
7 go to the gym
8 have lunch
9 take a nap
10 read a book

WRITING PRACTICE

B

Model answer

During the week, I wake up early every morning. I usually have coffee and some toast for breakfast. I sometimes listen to the radio as I get ready for work. I take a shower, get dressed and then drive to my office.
I'm often very busy at work, so when the office closes, I like to go for a swim to relax. There is a pool nearby. Then, I go home and have dinner with my husband. In the evening, I like to read a book or watch a little TV.
My routine on the weekend is very different. I get up late and visit friends or family. It's much more fun than going to work!

4.1 What do you do?

VOCABULARY

A

1 businesswoman **2** mechanic **3** dentist **4** engineer
5 hairdresser **6** teacher **7** journalist **8** nurse

B

1 office **2** home **3** travels **4** meetings **5** meet
6 wear **7** computer

C

a journalist **b** businesswoman **c** teacher **d** nurse

GRAMMAR

A

1 c or e **2** e or c **3** d **4** f **5** a **6** b

B

1 Does / doesn't **2** Do / do **3** Does / does **4** Do / don't

C

2 Does your sister work full time?
3 Do you wear a uniform at work?
4 Does your wife travel a lot for work?
5 Does your company have an office in New York?

PRONUNCIATION

2 Does she
3 Do you
4 Does he
5 Does she
6 Do you

4.2 Good job!

GRAMMAR

A

2 have to wear **3** doesn't have to work **4** don't have to pay
5 doesn't have to get up **6** has to travel

B

2 Do you have to do a lot of training?
3 Do you have to work inside?
4 Do you have to pay for tea and coffee?
5 Do you have to work nine to five?

PRONUNCIATION

1 answer **2** work **3** use **4** start **5** go **6** organize

VOCABULARY

A

1 d **2** a **3** e **4** b **5** c

B

1 early in the morning **2** noon **3** nine to five
4 midnight **5** late in the afternoon

4.3 Learn something new

GRAMMAR

A

1 Where **2** What **3** When **4** why **5** who **6** How long
7 How much

B

2 What do you do?
3 Why do you study English?
4 How long does it take to become a teacher?
5 How much does it cost?

PRONUNCIATION

1 Where do you study?
2 What do you study?
3 How long is your course?
4 Who is your teacher?
5 How much do you spend on books?
6 Why do you want to get a degree?

VOCABULARY

A

1 go **2** study **3** take **4** get **5** train

B

2 a degree **3** a business **4** an exam
5 a subject **6** a qualification

4.4 Reading

READING

A

2

B

1 a **2** c **3** b **4** a **5** c

C

1 role **2** 2,000 miles **3** $35,000 **4** round-trip flights
5 a uniform **6** contact

4.5 Listening; Functional Language

LISTENING

A

his current job, his work hours, the job he would like, the size of his company

B

1 F (He doesn't work as an actor on TV. / He works as a receptionist.)
2 F (He works in an office.)
3 T
4 T
5 F (He has an hour for lunch at noon.)
6 F (The company is very big.)
7 F (He doesn't think his job is very interesting.)
8 T

FUNCTIONAL LANGUAGE

R = Receptionist RK = Richard Kershaw

1 R: Good morning. This is Schmidt and Brandt. Can I help you?
2 RK: Hello. Could I speak to Hannah Schmidt, please?
3 R: Who's speaking, please?
4 RK: It's Richard Kershaw.
5 R: Hold on a minute, please.
6 R: I'm afraid she isn't available right now. Would you like to leave a message?
7 RK: Yes, please. Can you ask her to call Richard from S-REK Ltd at 800-555-0199, please?
8 R: I'm sorry, can you repeat that?

4.6 Write an email asking for information

WRITING

A

1 learn **2** skills **3** four **4** morning **5** contact

B

time of classes, how much the classes cost,
what languages they teach

C

Dear Ms. Souza,
I am writing to ask about your language classes. First, what languages do you offer? Do you have French classes? Second, when are your classes? I am free in the evenings and on the weekend. Do you have classes on Saturdays and Sundays? Finally, how much does the course cost?
I look forward to hearing from you.
All the best,
Pieter Hines

D

1 Greeting and the name of the person you are writing to
2 Reason for writing
3 Asking about the language courses on offer
4 Asking about the times of classes on offer
5 Asking about the cost of the courses
6 Standard 'end of letter' phrase

WRITING PRACTICE

C

Model answer

Dear Ms. Nagy,
I am writing to ask about your two-day professional interview course. First, how much does the course cost? Second, when is the course? Is it during the week or on the weekend? Finally, where is the course held?
I look forward to hearing from you.
Kind regards,
Alex

5.1 There's no place like home

VOCABULARY

A

1 armchair **2** bathtub **3** fridge **4** shower **5** bed **6** lamp **7** oven **8** toilet **9** dishwasher **10** couch

B

Bedroom	Bathroom	Kitchen	Living room
bed	bathtub	dishwasher	armchair
lamp	shower	fridge	couch
	toilet	lamp	lamp
		oven	

PRONUNCIATION

1 dad **2** blue **3** dig **4** gate **5** boat **6** got

GRAMMAR

A

1 is **2** isn't **3** aren't **4** Is **5** are **6** some **7** any **8** any **9** is **10** are

B

1 There are **2** there is **3** There isn't **4** there are **5** There is **6** there are **7** There aren't

5.2 My neighborhood

VOCABULARY

A

2 park **3** movie theater **4** library **5** subway station **6** supermarket **7** gym **8** museum

B

1 market **2** airport **3** hospital **4** restaurant **5** theater **6** stores

GRAMMAR

A

1 Lizzie can speak Spanish.
2 He can't ride a bike.
3 She can't sing.
4 He can't swim.
5 He can make sushi.
6 Sarah can play the violin.

B

1 We ~~go~~ can't **go** to the movie theater tonight because it's closed.
2 correct
3 David can ~~to~~ speak three languages, English, French and Korean. His mom is French and his dad is South Korean.
4 correct
5 She lives close to her office so she can walk~~s~~ to work in the morning.
6 I play the guitar and I'm in a band. **Can** ~~Do~~ you ~~can~~ play a musical instrument?

PRONUNCIATION

1 weak **2** strong **3** weak **4** strong **5** weak **6** strong **7** weak **8** strong

5.3 Amazing buildings

GRAMMAR

A

1 b
2 e
3 d
4 c
5 a

B

1 Turn **2** Listen **3** push **4** go **5** take **6** Buy **7** touch **8** be

VOCABULARY

1 modern **2** terrible **3** ugly **4** amazing **5** beautiful **6** strange

PRONUNCIATION

2 beautiful **3** amazing **4** ugly **5** interesting **6** strange

5.4 Reading

READING

A

b

B

1 d **2** b **3** d **4** a and d **5** c **6** a and d **7** b **8** b and c

C

1 $2,100 **2** gym **3** washing machine **4** bus **5** lock **6** bills **7** subway station **8** on-street

5.5 Listening; Functional Language

LISTENING

A

places to eat, street art, tourism, markets, transportation in the city, parks and green spaces

B

1 T
2 F (Hannah says there are a few amazing restaurants and some really good cafés.)
3 T
4 F (Victor lives in Montreal.)
5 T
6 F (Victor says there is lots of street art.)
7 F (Victor says there are some beautiful old buildings.)
8 T

FUNCTIONAL LANGUAGE

A

1 c **2** f **3** b **4** a **5** d **6** e

B

V = Victor H = Hannah

1 V: Hi Hannah! I'm at the subway station.
2 H: Oh, hey Victor! Do you need directions to my apartment?
3 V: Yes, please.
4 H: OK. Come out of the subway station. There is a bank across from the entrance.
5 V: … across from the subway station.
6 H: Cross over the road and turn left. Then take the first turn on the right.
7 V: First turn on the right …
8 H: Walk past the movie theater. It's on the left.
9 V: Movie theater on the right …
10 H: No, on the left. Walk to the end of the road. My apartment is on the left next to the café.

5.6 Write a description of a place

WRITING

A

2

B

famous, high, amazing, old, white, beautiful, red, gold, old, long, interesting, pretty, nice, quiet, great

C

2 Where is it?
3 What does it look like?
4 What can you see there? / What can you do there?
5 What is it like?

WRITING PRACTICE

C

Model answer

The Burj Khalifa is currently the tallest skyscraper in the world. It is in Dubai in the United Arab Emirates. There are wonderful views from the top floor. You can see the whole of Dubai, the ocean and the desert outside of the city.

The Burj Khalifa is made from glass, metal and concrete. The building gets narrow closer to the top. It has a total of 163 floors.

In front of the Burj Khalifa is a big, beautiful fountain. Inside there are restaurants, offices, a gym and even a hotel. It is an amazing building.

6.1 Let's go out

VOCABULARY

A

1 festival **2** exhibit **3** comedy show **4** theater **5** concert **6** movie theater

B

1 exhibit **2** theater **3** movie theater **4** festival **5** comedy show **6** concert

PRONUNCIATION

2 Oo
3 Ooo
4 ooOo
5 Oo
6 Oo

GRAMMAR

A

1 I don't like stay**ing** in all the time!
2 I love~~s~~ **going** to the movie theater.
3 They love~~s~~ ~~to~~ playing soccer.
4 He ~~not~~ **doesn't** like watch**ing** TV.
5 I hate~~s~~ pizza!
6 We ~~not~~ **don't** like visit**ing** museums.

B

1 Ahmad loves going to festivals.
2 He likes eating Italian food.
3 He doesn't like playing video games.
4 He hates going to the theater.
5 He hates listening to pop music.

6.2 It was fun

GRAMMAR

A

1 Where were your parents born?
2 My train was really busy this morning.
3 I was in Tokyo for business last month.
4 The tickets were really expensive!
5 How was the concert last night?
6 That was a really terrible movie!
7 It was really hot all last week.

B

2 were **3** wasn't **4** was **5** weren't **6** was **7** was **8** wasn't **9** were **10** was **11** were **12** wasn't

PRONUNCIATION

1 /wʌz/
2 /wəz/
3 /wər/
4 /wɜːr/
5 /wər/
6 /wɜːr/
7 /wʌz/
8 /wʌz/

VOCABULARY

A

1 in **2** in **3** ago **4** Last **5** in **6** ago

B

1 The first Oscar ceremony was ~~last~~ **in** 1929.
2 They were at the movie theater ~~in~~ **last** night.
3 correct
4 correct
5 Peter was at college five years ~~last~~ **ago**.
6 correct

6.3 Life stories

GRAMMAR

A

1 was
2 started / began
3 reached
4 moved
5 began / started
6 worked
7 made
8 won
9 died
10 released

B

1 took **2** went **3** moved **4** bought **5** saw **6** started
7 met **8** won

PRONUNCIATION

1 /ɪd/
2 /t/
3 /t/
4 /d/
5 /d/
6 /d/
7 /t/
8 /ɪd/

VOCABULARY

1 went **2** studied **3** started **4** became **5** got **6** moved
7 was **8** had

6.4 Reading

READING

A

1 *Laugh Night* **2** *The Blade* **3** *3200*

B

1 T
2 F (The writer recommends *3200*.)
3 T
4 F (The writer didn't think *Laugh Night* was funny.)
5 F (The writer wasn't surprised that *The Blade* was so good.)
6 T

C

1 Emma Davies
2 Damian Shultz (and) Greta Simons
3 Ivan Rodriguez
4 Tosh Ellis

6.5 Listening; Functional Language

LISTENING

A

1 The actors **2** The special effects **3** The music
4 The director

B

1 a **2** b **3** a **4** b **5** c **6** c

FUNCTIONAL LANGUAGE

2 loved **3** awful **4** about **5** sure
6 awesome **7** think **8** OK **9** hate

6.6 Write a review of an event

WRITING

B

People throw tomatoes at each other.

C

1 F (Laura went to the festival with three of her friends.)
2 F (The ticket cost $175, which included three nights at the hotel.)
3 F (They stayed in a hotel in Valencia.)
4 T
5 F (The whole event lasted an hour.)
6 T

D

1 c **2** e **3** a **4** b **5** d

E

first, next, then, after that, finally

F

1 First, we waited in the line to get into the venue.
2 Next, actors dressed in 1920s costumes showed us to our seats.
3 Then, we watched the first half of the movie.
4 After that, we had dinner while a live band played music from the movie.
5 Finally, we watched the end of the movie. It was a great night.

WRITING PRACTICE

B

Model answer

Last year I went to the Edinburgh Festival Fringe in Scotland for the first time. It is the largest arts festival in the world. I went there with my friend Maria.
We stayed in a guesthouse near the city center. It was fairly expensive as thousands of people come to Edinburgh for the festival. There are lots of different shows to go and see, but it is mostly famous for its comedy shows. Some of the shows are free and some cost around $60.
The venues are all over the city so you should plan your day carefully. The festival goes on for 25 days in August.
After the festival ends, prizes are awarded to the performers, for example best show, best joke, etc. It was a great experience and I'd love to go again.

Notes

Notes

Notes